MW00610610

Finding What Matters

The *Finding What Matters* series explores the Scriptures to discover what matters most to God. The studies in this series are in-depth in nature and will cause the individual to look deeply at their inner person. These studies help the believer to understand how to live out the things that matter most to God; to love God with abandon and others without reservation, to live under the Lordship of Jesus Christ and to fulfill the very reason He created them. The *Finding What Matters* series is based on Colossians 3:1-17.

Therefore if you have been raised up with Christ, keep seeking the things above, where Christ is, seated at the right hand of God. Set your mind on the things above, not on the things that are on earth. For you have died and your life is hidden with Christ in God. When Christ, who is our life, is revealed, then you also will be revealed with Him in glory.

Therefore consider the members of your earthly body as dead to immorality, impurity, passion, evil desire, and greed, which amounts to idolatry. For it is because of these things that the wrath of God will come upon the sons of disobedience, and in them you also once walked, when you were living in them. But now you also, put them all aside: anger, wrath, malice, slander, and abusive speech from your mouth. Do not lie to one another, since you laid aside the old self with its evil practices, and have put on the new self who is being renewed to a true knowledge according to the image of the One who created him— a renewal in which there is no distinction between Greek and Jew, circumcised and uncircumcised, barbarian, Scythian, slave and freeman, but Christ is all, and in all.

So, as those who have been chosen of God, holy and beloved, put on a heart of compassion, kindness, humility, gentleness and patience; bearing with one another, and forgiving each other, whoever has a complaint against anyone; just as the Lord forgave you, so also should you. Beyond all these things put on love, which is the perfect bond of unity. Let the peace of Christ rule in your hearts, to which indeed you were called in one body; and be thankful. Let the word of Christ richly dwell within you, with all wisdom teaching and admonishing one another with psalms and hymns and spiritual songs, singing with thankfulness in your hearts to God. Whatever you do in word or deed, do all in the name of the Lord Jesus, giving thanks through Him to God the Father.

— Colossians 3:1-17 nasb

Studies in the Finding What Matters series:

Being Renewed
Embracing the Love of God
Living with Abandon

DEREK PUBLISHING

Being Renewed; Finding What Matters Series
Copyright © 2009 as Learning to Love and Be Loved. Revision Copyright © 2015 as Being
Renewed — Ancient Promise Ministries. All rights reserved.
Printed in the United States of America.

No part of this publication may be reproduced, stored in a retrieval system or transmitted
in any form or by any means (electronic, mechanical, photocopying, recording, or
otherwise) without the prior written permission of the publisher; Derek Publishing.

Requests for information should be addressed to:
Derek Publishing, 2945 Bell Road #145, Auburn, California 95603
email: derekpublishing@gmail.com, web: derekpublishing.co

Library of Congress Cataloging-in-Publication Data

Names: Content Co-Created for Ancient Promise Ministries
Title: Being Renewed; Finding What Matters Series
Identifiers: ISBN's Workbook: 978-1-946561-05-3
Subjects: Religious / Education / Christian Essentials / Leadership Training

All Scripture quotations, unless otherwise indicated are taken from The ESV® Bible
(The Holy Bible, English Standard Version®) copyright © 2001 by Crossway Bibles, a
publishing ministry of Good News Publishers. ESV®Text Edition: 2007. The ESV® text
has been reproduced in cooperation with and by permission of Good News Publishers.
Used by permission. All rights reserved. The ESV® Bible (The Holy Bible, English
Standard Version®) is adapted from the Revised Standard Version of the Bible, copyright
Division of Christian Education of the National Council of the Churches of Christ in the
U.S.A. All rights reserved.

Scripture quotations marked "NASB" are taken from the New American Standard Bible®,
Copyright © 1960, 1962, 1963, 1968, 1971, 1972, 1973, 1975, 1977, 1995 by The
Lockman Foundation. Used by permission.

Scripture quotations marked "NIV" are taken from the Holy Bible, New International
Version®, NIV®. Copyright © 1973, 1978, 1984, 2011 by Biblica, Inc.™ Used by
permission of Zondervan. All rights reserved worldwide. www.zondervan.com The "NIV"
and "New International Version" are trademarks registered in the United States Patent and
Trademark Office by Biblica, Inc.™

derek
PUBLISHING

Ancient Promise Discipleship Curricula is published for
Ancient Promise Ministries by Derek Publishing. The curricula has been
translated into several languages and has been used to equip church
leaders in Tanzania, Kenya, Ethiopia, Uganda, India and Mexico.
For more information about Ancient Promise Ministries
visit ancientpromise.org
For more information about the curricula visit derekpublishing.co

Finding What Matters
Being Renewed

TABLE *of* CONTENTS

Finding What Matters
Being Renewed

Introduction

The boundless love of God, so rich and pure, is woven throughout the pages of the Bible from the Old Testament to the end of the New. The love of God, His tender kindness and overwhelming grace, draw us inexplicably to Him. The richness of His love will cause the darkest soul to turn away from lifestyles enveloped in darkness to walk with Him in the kingdom of His marvelous light.

> [16] I pray that out of his glorious riches he may strengthen you with power through his Spirit in your inner being, [17] so that Christ may dwell in your hearts through faith. And I pray that you, being rooted and established in love, [18] may have power, together with all the Lord's holy people, to grasp how wide and long and high and deep is the love of Christ, [19] and to know this love that surpasses knowledge—that you may be filled to the measure of all the fullness of God.
>
> — Ephesians 3:16-19 NIV

God tells us through the writer Paul that we can know this wondrous love as an experience in our inner being. What an amazing truth. The God of all creation has made it possible to know Him deeply. He has made it possible to experience a love relationship with Him that can fill our innermost being to overflowing and in that filling change us forever!

If we are to live in this relationship it obviously cannot be a one-sided experience. When questioned about what mattered most to God, Jesus answered:

> "Love the Lord your God with all your heart and with all your soul and with all your mind and with all your strength.' The second is this: 'Love your neighbor as yourself.' There is no commandment greater than these."
>
> — Mark 12:30-31 NIV

His response does not seem hard or complicated, yet it is indeed a much more difficult task than we will often admit.

Something happened to mankind in the Garden of Eden that has destroyed his ability to know and experience this love relationship with God. After man chose to sin, his perception and view of God and himself changed forever. Man's sin brought shame into his life and drove him away to hide from his creator. Sin and selfishness entered the soul of man driving him even further from the presence of the One he had loved, the very

One who had loved him fully. But God came and called out to Adam as he was walking in the Garden: "Adam where are you?"

God was not blind to what Adam had done – He wasn't even surprised – but you can almost hear a grief and longing in His voice as He called out to Adam to come and walk with Him.

God is calling His creation to come back to the Garden to walk with Him again. He calls us to know Him and be known by Him. God beckons His children back to His loving embrace. He longs for His creation.

Is it possible to experience and know Him as Adam did in the Garden today? Many would say no and in some sense this is true. Innocence has been lost. However, throughout the Gospels, Acts, and the Epistles, it is evident that when people truly experienced God's presence they were forever changed. The change was not just outward appearances, behavior modification, or the refocusing of selfish desires and habits to more socially acceptable ones, but a true change of their internal nature. In John the Apostle's writings, we see that when we submit to God as an expression of love for Him, He dwells within us and we love both God and each other more. The very evidence of the presence of God in our lives is directly related to our loving obedience to Him and the way that we love each other. Yes, we can walk with Him again in a wondrous loving relationship. And through that experience of Him we can be completely transformed into people who love as He loves.

The Apostle Paul gives us a very clear picture of this transformational process in Colossians 3:1-4, giving us the very foundation of this study.

> ¹ Therefore if you have been raised up with Christ, keep seeking the things above, where Christ is, seated at the right hand of God. ² Set your mind on the things above, not on the things that are on earth. ³ For you have died and your life is hidden with Christ in God. ⁴ When Christ, who is our life, is revealed, then you also will be revealed with Him in glory.

First, we see that when we place our faith in Christ at salvation, we are raised up with Christ, giving us a new position seated next to Him. Because of this new position we are to continuously seek the things above, which brings to us a new perspective – His perspective. Then we are to set our minds – which in the Greek means affections, will, and moral considerations – based on the things above. This perspective happens when we die to ourselves and our lives are hidden in Christ with God. The new life we receive is His life in us, giving us a new image – His image – revealed here on earth. When His life is revealed here on earth through us, He will reveal us with Him in glory or heaven.

This study is designed to help us understand why it is so difficult to love God with complete abandon and others without reservation. Its purpose is to help us discover what God desires from His children and how to allow His Spirit to renew our minds and transform our souls so that we are able to love as He has commanded.

> 22 "The eye is the lamp of the body; so then if your eye is clear, your whole body will be full of light. 23 But if your eye is bad, your whole body will be full of darkness. If then the light that is in you is darkness, how great is the darkness!
>
> — MATTHEW 6:22-23 NASB

Soul transformation begins with changing our perspective to be His perspective. We need to see things from above where we are seated next to Him in the light of His presence.

Each lesson in the study is broken into 4 segments. The first segment will explore what God has intended for us as His crowning creation. This segment is called *God's Intent*. In the second segment, *The Condition of Man*, we will explore the condition of man based on man's rebellion in the Garden of Eden. The third segment focuses on how we struggle even as believers in Christ, because of our condition passed down to us by Adam. This segment is called *The Struggle Within*. In the final segment, we will ask questions of our inner life to see how we are personally being impacted because of our condition. This final segment is called *A Look Inside*.

Philosophy of Material

As you begin this study, please remember that God revealed to us His plan of salvation from sin, which brings eternal life with Him. This salvation involves three aspects of the human condition. When we believe in the substitutionary death of Christ on the cross, by His grace we are saved from the penalty of sin, which brings spiritual life in Christ. This is called justification. When we submit to the continuous renewing work of His Spirit that transforms us into the image of His Son, we are being saved from the power of sin. This is called sanctification. When we die physically and enter into eternity we will be saved from the presence of sin. This is called glorification. This study focuses on the second aspect of our salvation – sanctification.

Being Renewed has been written with soul transformation in mind. In this study we will seek to gain a clear understanding of what it means to be renewed and walk through the transformation process. Because this study has been written with a focus on renewal and soul transformation, please know that even though it is based completely on the Word of God, it is not a theological study. This study is also not designed or intended for a self-help support group. It is indeed a Bible Study. It is a journey through the Word of God to help us understand how God, through His Word and His Spirit, can renew, transform, and fill our souls. We will be dealing with the "inner man" as Paul calls our soul. This is the process of "putting off the old self with its practices and putting on the new self, which is being renewed in knowledge after the image of its creator" from Colossians 3:10.

In the lessons to follow we will seek to understand how the way we love God and others can determine our experience of life and the soul satisfaction we hunger for. We will uncover the places we have run to in our relationships, and in our pursuit of meaning and purpose that have left us empty and unchanged. We will discover what it means to submit to the work of Christ in our lives as we grow in our understanding of His design and desire to restore our relationship to Him and ultimately His image in us.

Ground Rules

Before we begin we need to establish some ground rules. We are going to look at Scriptures many of you know by heart, however, please take the time to:

1. Look at these passages as if you had never seen them before. Assume you don't know what they mean so you can see them in a fresh way. Break the homework up by sections to be completed over 3 – 4 days.

2. When you look at the personal questions, put down what you feel to be true within your soul instead of trying to put down what you think is right or what others would want to see. Right answers without a true understanding of their meaning are often not right answers at all. Real answers are the ones that will uncover what is truly going on inside.

3. Write down your answers thoroughly. They are between you and the Lord. It is important you write them down. Take your time and reflect thoroughly on your answers.

4. This is a topical reflective study. You will be asked to reflect on very specific questions designed to cause you to evaluate your own experience of the truth you have discovered. For those who are used to inductive and deductive Bible study, and are therefore used to analyzing the details of the verse and those around it, answer the questions first before you go deeper, so you are not distracted from the intent of the question.

5. You will also need to find someone who will walk through this with you. Galatians 6:2 tells us to "bear one another's burdens and to gently and humbly help each other back onto the right path." James 5:16 says to "confess your sins to each other and pray for each other so that you may be healed." Healing is not always physical.

There is a war waging throughout all of God's creation over the souls of men. Satan seeks to destroy what God has created. He was cast from heaven to the earth when he tried to raise his throne above God's. Our enemy's greatest desire is to destroy God's most precious creation — man. He desires to keep you from experiencing and fulfilling the very reason you were created. The war is on.

Understanding Our Condition
His Design

1

God's Intent

Before there was beginning, there was God. God in all His wonder and glory existed in Himself. He was in no need of anything or anyone. However God within His being is a Creator. When we look at what is revealed about Him throughout His Word, we see that He existed before all things and He created all things. Nothing exists apart from this transcendent infinite Creator God.

> 20 "My prayer is not for them alone. I pray also for those who will believe in me through their message, 21 that all of them may be one, Father, just as you are in me and I am in you. May they also be in us so that the world may believe that you have sent me. 22 I have given them the glory that you gave me, that they may be one as we are one— 23 I in them and you in me—so that they may be brought to complete unity. Then the world will know that you sent me and have loved them even as you have loved me.
>
> — JOHN 17:20-23 NIV

After God spoke into existence all form and matter and every living thing, He looked over all that He had done and it was good. Then He said, "Let Us make man in Our image." God took the elements that He had created and did more than speak. God formed with His hands His crowning creation and breathed His own breath into his body. He gave man physical life, soul life, and spiritual life. Man was made a living breathing being that could respond and relate to his Creator. Why would God do such a thing? Why would He create us in His image?

When we think of the vastness of all that He has made, why would God create a being for the purpose of bearing His image? Could it be that God wanted to be known through a soul that was like His own? Could it be that God wanted to be loved by someone who had the capacity to love in the same way that He loves? God is sufficient within His own existence. He knows intimacy and love within the Godhead in ways that cannot be fathomed by our finite human minds and therefore does not need man's love (John 17:20-23). Yet He created us in His image. He placed us in an environment in the Garden where He walked with us, talked with us, and delighted in the relationship He shared with us. It seems that God created us to be loved and to reflect His loving nature as we respond to Him.

1. Read Genesis 1:24-27.

   Record: 1) what you see about God and 2) what He was doing.

   _____

   _____

   _____

   _____

   _____

The Condition of Man

Because God has designed man to live in relationship with both Him and others, He has also created man to experience Him and His provision in a way that can only be satisfied by Him. As we have stated, God took very special care when He created man. He was intimately involved in the creation as He formed him from the earth and breathed spiritual life into his being. God intentionally created the soul of man to be satisfied in ways that only He has the capacity to fill and only in the ways He has ordained.

1. With that in mind, read Genesis 2:7-8, 15-24 and answer the following questions.

   a. What was different about the way God created man?

   _____

   _____

   b. Where was man placed and what was it like?

   _____

   _____

   _____

   c. What was man to do?

   _____

   _____

   _____

   d. What did God do for the man to deal with his loneliness?

   _____

   _____

As we read these verses we can see in the creation story that God created man with a specific purpose. He was to cultivate and keep the Garden of Eden; he was to name the animals and subdue the earth. This created in man a sense of purpose; his life had meaning and significance outside of himself.

God placed man in the Garden. He gave him a specific place where he was to live. He gave him someone "after his own kind" – someone he could relate to. He gave him someone with whom He could identify with and belong to. God made man with value and belonging, creating within him the capacity to love and be loved.

We can also see that God provided for man's basic needs for existence. He gave them provision for their appetites; food, water and a sexual partner to enjoy as together they subdued and populated the earth. God gave them each other to share life with and through this relationship they would fill each other's loneliness. They had a specific place to exist (home), and the safety and security of the Garden.

In the *God's Design* graphic you can see that God has created us to relate to Him spiritually, emotionally and physically. Below is a summary explanation.

God's Design

Significance	Spiritual Well-being
Position	Man was created with a spiritual position in relationship to God. He walked next to God and had a specific place in God's order of things.
Purpose	Man was created to fulfill a specific purpose in God's plan.
Meaning	Man knew his life had meaning and that there was more to life than the immediate – God had placed eternity in his heart.
Value	**Emotional Well-being**
Loved	Man was loved and cared for.
Belongs	Man belonged in relationship with God and others.
Enough	Man was all he needed to be – he was enough.
Provision	**Physical Well-being**
Appetites	Man needs food, water and sex
Shelter	Man needs shelter and protection from the elements
Safety	Man needs security, stability and health

Significance, value and provision are at the very core of man's existence. They are placed deep within man's inner being, causing him to have longing and appetite. These core elements are neither right nor wrong but were placed in man so that he would look beyond himself. This inner being is referred to as the "soul" in the Bible. It is the seat of man's nature.

The Inner Man

In this lesson we will look at how our soul has been created to relate specifically to the God of all creation. We will see what it means to be created in His image and how important it is to allow our souls to respond to God in a loving relationship. We will see how the condition of our soul affects our ability to respond to God, as He desires.

Before we look at the soul of man, it is important to understand that we cannot know the precise way in which the soul exists and functions. Scholars differ on how they define it, so take this into consideration as you work through the concept explanations.

Man has been created with three very distinct arenas from which life is experienced; body, spirit and soul. While these arenas are distinct they are completely interdependent and do not function separately from each other.

Body	The **body** allows us to interact with and experience the world around us through our senses. This interaction is then taken into the soul where we process this information based on the condition of our soul.
Spirit	The **spirit** is where man is made alive to God at salvation. It is here that we interact with and experience the spiritual world. These experiences are taken into the soul and processed based on the condition of our soul.
Soul	The **soul** is where the mind, emotions, and will process the experiences of the body and spirit. This is where we think (mind) based on how we feel (emotion) about an experience and determine (will) how to react or respond.

Man has been uniquely designed to relate to God. God created man with a physical being; a body with senses. God has chosen to manifest Himself at various times in various ways in a tangible visible presence; God the Son could be seen, felt and heard. God created man with a soul; he has a mind and intellect, emotions (heart) and will. God in His being has a mind, emotions and will. God created man a spiritual being. Man has an invisible eternal essence. God is Spirit and is invisible and eternal.

There are three distinct personalities in the Godhead, yet there is only one God. In his book The Knowledge of the Holy A. W. Tozer says, "All that God is does all that God does." They cannot be separated from each other and do not work independently. This is one of those mysteries that we must be content to only understand in a very limited way.

God has uniquely created us to respond to Him in relationship.

2. Look up the following passages and record how the Triune God has made Himself relatable.

   a. John 1:14-18

   _____

   _____

   _____

b. John 4:23-24

_____

_____

_____

c. Hebrews 1:1-3

_____

_____

_____

That God would go to such lengths to be known by His creation is beyond comprehension. It says so much about Him and His care for us. God became flesh and blood so we could see, touch, and hear Him. He sent His Son so we could know what He is like, what He is doing, and what is important to Him. He came so we would know what an intimate loving relationship could be like as He lived in relationship with the Father and then loved those around Him. He came to make it possible to know Him through His death on the cross and gave His Spirit to live in us. God wants to be known by His creation! God has been revealing Himself to His creation since the beginning. God is infinite and transcendent. He is beyond our ability to understand fully, yet He makes Himself known.

The Struggle Within

Man has been specifically designed to live in a dependent loving relationship with God. In this relationship man will live out his purpose and find his soul is at home. In this relationship, man's soul can experience its deepest fulfillment.

However, something happened to destroy that relationship. And when it did, the image of God in man, though still imprinted in us, was marred and distorted by sin. When Adam and Eve rebelled against God, they brought sin into this world and man's spirit died.

The understanding of death in the Bible does not mean, "to cease to exist." It means, "to be separated from." If we die physically, our spirit and soul are separated from the body; if we are dead spiritually, our spirit and soul are separated from God.

1. Look up the verses below and describe what happened to man's soul and his relationship with God.

    a. Romans 5:12-14

_____

_____

_____

_____

    b.   Hebrews 2:15

_____

_____

_____

    c.   John 3:19

_____

_____

Because of sin, man's entire being has been completely changed. His body now dies physically because of sin's affect. His soul is darkened and his spirit is separated from his Creator.

The Image of Christ In Us

But there is hope! When we receive forgiveness of sin through faith in Jesus and His death on the cross, all of our sins are forgiven and we no longer pay the penalty for the sin we have committed against God and others. The Spirit of Living God comes into our souls and joins with our spirit, becoming the Life within us. He begins to renew His image in our soul and gives us a new nature—His.

2.   Read the following verses and summarize what you learn.

    a.   Colossians 3:9-10

_____

_____

_____

    b.   II Corinthians 3:17-18

_____

_____

_____

_____

_____

We become a new creation that has the capacity again to relate to God and bear His image clearly. However, the process of living as a new creation requires that God do some powerful and radical work on the soul of man. Understanding what He is doing and why, will help us join with His Spirit as we learn to trust Him.

As we read Psalm 63:1-8, we can't help but see that David simultaneously experienced the presence of Living God, and also longed for Living God. He experienced deep soul satisfaction while basking in the glory of this loving yet powerful God. This in turn caused him to hunger for God all the more.

Can you imagine what it would be like to have your soul satisfied as with "fat and rich food?" What would it be like for your soul to be so filled and your inner longing so met that it would cause you to long for that experience in the same way you would thirst for water in a desert? If your soul thirsted in this way it would mean what you longed for was a matter of life and death! Do you long for the presence of God like this?

3. Read Psalm 63:1-8. Record what it tells you about the relationship between God and David.

_____

_____

4. Read Psalm 139.

    a. Describe how God sees David.

    _____

    _____

    _____

    b. Describe how David views God.

    _____

    _____

    _____

    c. Summarize what this passage indicates about David's relationship with God.

    _____

    _____

    _____

    _____

5. Read Ecclesiastes 3:11. Record what "eternity written in our hearts" does to man.

_____

_____

_____

God has put the imprint of His image within the inner being of man. Because of sin, that image is marred and distorted. Man will never be complete or satisfied with this life apart from a restored relationship with the One who loves him fully. He will hunger and thirst for more and yet nothing will be enough until he is restored.

God has created man in His image so that He can enjoy a relationship with him. He has placed eternity in his heart so he would long for things beyond himself, so that he would long for eternal God, his Creator.

A Look Inside

At the end of each lesson you will be asked questions that will help you discover what lies in your own soul. These questions are designed to guide you in a self-discovery process so you can understand the things God wants you to know as His Spirit reveals, restores and transforms you. Please spend time on these questions. Let them sink in as you seek to be honest before the Lord.

1. In order to evaluate the condition of your relationship with God and others please prayerfully answer the following questions:

    a. What things tend to be the reasons you are drawn to someone? Why?

    _____

    _____

    _____

    _____

    _____

    _____

    _____

    b. What are the most important things you believe you need to know about someone in order to be close in relationship?

    _____

    _____

    _____

    _____

    _____

    _____

    _____

    _____

    _____

c. What things about God drew you to Christ in relationship? Why?

_____

_____

_____

_____

_____

_____

_____

d. Briefly describe how you came to faith in Christ

_____

_____

_____

_____

_____

_____

_____

e. What are the characteristics found in a meaningful relationship?

_____

_____

_____

_____

_____

_____

f. Are these characteristics found in your relationship with God?
Explain your answer.

_____

_____

_____

_____

_____

_____

_____

_____

_____

_____

As you reflect on God's design, please remember that He is faithful and will complete the work He has started in you. Our part, as His children, is to trust His ability to do the work, agree with Him because He is right and good, and obey Him even when we don't completely understand. He wants us to know Him as much as we are known by Him. This experiential knowledge of trusting Him will renew His image in us.

Understanding Our Condition
Driven By Fear   *2*

God's Intent

God created man in His image so that he could have the capacity to know God and be known by God. He wrote eternity in man's heart so that he would seek, and in that seeking would find and know eternal God. God desired a pure relationship of love with man; a relationship that was unhindered by selfishness or shame. He desired to live in a relationship with another being who had the capacity to reason and choose and in the choosing, would choose Him above all else. God desired to delight in His creation and have a spiritual oneness with that creation that can only be seen in the Godhead. God said, "Let Us make man in Our image."

> ²⁶ Then God said, "Let us make mankind in our image, in our likeness, so that they may rule over the fish in the sea and the birds in the sky, over the livestock and all the wild animals, and over all the creatures that move along the ground." ²⁷ So God created mankind in his own image, in the image of God he created them; male and female he created them.
>
> — GENESIS 1:26-27 NIV

Living in Oneness

In Genesis 2:25 we see a description of the condition of man's soul when he was first created.

"And the man and his wife were both naked and they were not ashamed."

The word ashamed in Hebrew means, "to be disgraced or disfigured." It means to have shattered human emotions, to feel guilt over sin or dismay and disappointment that things are not what they seemed. It is the disappointment that something or someone did not live up to a standard or expectation. It could also be defined as having one's value or worth diminished or destroyed.

The context of this statement was that the man and his wife were naked and unashamed as they lived with each other and with God. In their original state before sin entered the world, even as they lived exposed, man and woman lived together with God completely at peace with how they were created. Neither of them desired to be anything other than what they were. The question of worth and value never entered their minds. They didn't wonder about the meaning of their lives. They had no need to protect themselves. There was no shame in their bodies or in what they looked like, and yet there was not an ounce of pride. They actually did not think about themselves at all. You will also notice they were completely content with each other.

As we look at what God desires for us today, we can know His priority is to restore the intimacy and beauty of this relationship.

1. Read John 17:21-26 and describe:

    a. The relationship seen in the Godhead.

    _____

    _____

    b. The relationship Jesus asks the disciples to have with the Father.

    _____

    _____

    c. The relationship Jesus asks the disciples to have with each other.

    _____

    _____

2. Look up the word unity or oneness and write a brief summary definition below.

    _____

    _____

    _____

    _____

    _____

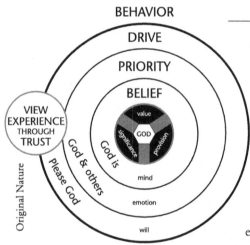

From the beginning, God desired both love and unity to be the foundation of our relationship with Him, as well as in all of our other relationships. God desired for us to know Him in innocent wonder and delight. God longed to move freely unhindered before our eyes. He longed to see His own reflection when He looked into our eyes. This could only happen through a relationship grounded in complete trust.

Review the *Original Nature* graphic. This graphic shows what our relationship was like at creation before sin entered the world.

VIEW	Significance, value and provision are viewed through trust
BELIEF	God is in control, cares and will determine how my needs are met
PRIORITY	God and others are important to me
DRIVE	I will do what pleases God
BEHAVIOR	Compassion, Kindness, Gentleness, Love

The Condition of Man

Something happened that shattered the trust and oneness that God had with His creation. His image in man became marred and distorted causing man's view of life, others, and God to be darkened and forever changed. Fear would replace trust and be passed down to all generations.

The article below was written by Diana Berns as she considered the question: "How did evil enter into the world if God did not create it?"

His Intent

It was meant to be. In the beginning you were with Me and you knew Me. You basked in My glory the light of My love, and delighted in My presence. You trusted Me, adored Me and I moved through you. You were My delight and everything was very good.

You had love, joy, peace, patience, kindness, gentleness and self-control. No law was needed. No need to protect or give limitations for such expressions. This freedom of movement is light and deep breath like warm wind that blows through your being. It is safety and comfort. Like a welcomed song it moves in a rhythmic dance like waves of consistent vibration that penetrate to the core of your being.

Why did you doubt Me? Why didn't you trust? Why did you look to your own understanding? Did you know what you would lose? My heart broke that day. I wasn't angry. I was hurt. I was grieved for the loss of the relationship we had, and My heart ached and longed to be with you.

You didn't comprehend what you would lose. Your freedom was lost that day. You doubted and fear took over. The liar was telling a partial truth, which is a lie and you believed the master of deceit. You would know good and evil just like Me. I wanted to shield you from this reality and enjoy you and be enjoyed by you. This knowing of evil created a fear so deep that you would forever see through its distorted lens. You wanted to return to Me but the guilt of your willing disobedience overtook you. Shame caused you to hide from Me. The lens of fear distorts the light. It is contrary to light and lacks freedom of movement. The shades of deep grey push down, hold back and resist with unrestrained questions about My intentions.

I designed you with unique abilities and wondrous qualities. Why wouldn't I want to be with you and delight in your discovery of Me. The day that fear took hold your curiosity and wonder shifted from delight to suspicion. You were not made to be afraid. You feared the unseen world and now you don't trust Me. Your rebellion opened your eyes to a world unleashing evil that you wish you had never seen. Why didn't I warn you? Why didn't I tell you what would happen when you ate from that tree? Did I want you to fail? Blame ravished your ability to relate to Me. Every Word I have spoken would be misinterpreted through this lens. How could I expect you to see through it?

Shame disfigured and fear distorted, the lens of the soul so dark. The enemy threw the first punch and the souls of all men would wear the mark of the first blow and see through the lens of the first rebellious act. The world once taken in with great anticipation is now shrouded in a veil of uncertainty. Beauty and excellence defiled, movement hindered. Helpless and hopeless in a haze of your own making, while the power of rebellious defiance, keeps you from My light.

If you could only see what I intended. If only you could understand My purpose. If only you could experience the safety of My presence and trust My love. The light of My presence melts away fear and alleviates doubt. If you knew Me I would give you understanding. I would show you Myself and you would never doubt. I so desire to be known by you. Allow me to move closer to you, touch you, let Me know you. Talk with Me.

Something had to be done. I want to relieve you of the pain and confusion your rebellion has caused, and break the curse you were placed under. My child, it is not good for you to continue in fear. Look to My Son. Find Me. I have made Myself known. I have made My purposes known. I have given you My Word so you could see My heart.

The One, the Perfect, the Holy planted Himself like a gem hidden in human form. An ingenious plan set in motion at the beginning of time to dispel the darkness from the inside out. The light hidden in this gem was no ordinary life. He spoke to His own about what was inevitable. Jesus said "I tell you the truth, unless a kernel of wheat falls to the ground and dies, it remains only a single seed. But if it dies, it produces many seeds." (John 12:24) With the force of an atomic bomb the light of His life was unleashed when the outer shell was destroyed. The curse was broken over the land, over His own, and freedom was offered to those who were once held captive in a dark kingdom.

Where the Spirit of the Lord is, there is freedom!

What happened in those moments changed everything, for all people, for all time.

Let's go back to the Garden of Eden and see what happened when sin entered into man's soul. This will help us understand what affects us today. When Adam and Eve lived in the Garden, they lived without fear. But now fear and shame have entered man's soul. Where did it come from and what is its source?

In the last lesson, we learned that God created man to experience life with Him.

- **Spiritually:** Man experienced spiritual significance. He was created with a position in relationship to God. He was given a purpose and was to fulfill that purpose eternally: his life had meaning.

- **Emotionally:** Man experienced value. He knew that he was unconditionally loved and belonged in relationship to God, others and his environment. He was created exactly as he should be—he was good enough in his own eyes and the eyes of others.

- **Physically:** Man experienced provision. His basic physical appetites were met, he had shelter from the elements and was in a safe place.

When man experiences life in this way, he finds peace in his spirit and rest for his soul and body. But here is the problem—he was also designed to experience all these things through God and by God. God created us this way so that we would seek for something beyond ourselves and ultimately find Him.

1. Read the following passages and record what happened to man's relationship to God. Genesis 3:7-13; 22-24

_____

_____

_____

_____

_____

_____

In verses 7-8, we see that man began to fear the presence of his creator because of the shame of his sin; he had lost his spiritual significance. He lost his position next to God and his God ordained purpose. In verses 9-13, we can see man had lost his place of belonging and his sense of unconditional love and value. Shame filled his soul and he would no longer feel like he was good enough to be loved. Now he would desperately strive for value and emotional need would fill his soul. In verse 23, we see that man lost his source of abundant provision. He would toil and sweat and worry that he would not have his physical needs met. Man would now view all of his experiences of people, life, and God through eyes blinded by fear, with desperate need filling his soul.

Study the *Nature of Adam* graphic.

VIEW	The need for significance, value and provision is viewed through fear
BELIEF	**I** am in control and determine what my needs are and how they are met
PRIORITY	**Me**—I can have whatever I feel will meet my need
DRIVE	I will please **myself**
BEHAVIOR	Self-focus, Judgment, Control, Demand. I seek: Power & Position, People & Performance, and Possessions & Pleasure

In addition to the fear that our needs will not be met, there also resides deep within our souls a shame that is difficult to overcome. At the core of every human's experience is the shame of a disfigured or marred soul.

In Genesis 3:7-10 we see that when man's eyes were opened knowing good and evil, shame suddenly filled and disfigured his soul. He was no longer content in what he had and how he had been created. His focus became inward. He would now view life, others and God, through the eyes of his need. He would then be consumed with his own need for significance, value and the satisfaction of his fleshly appetites.

If we are to experience unhindered intimacy with our God and others, we must deal with the part of our being that has become marred and disfigured by sin. We must deal with the fear that springs forth from a soul clothed in and filled with shame.

After Adam sinned, God called him back to the Garden to walk with Him in the cool of the evening, naked and unashamed, but Adam hid himself from the presence of God and fashioned fig leaves to cover his shame (Genesis 3:8-10). Scripture tells us we are born into sin. This means the nature within us at birth is driven and motivated by fear and shame which leads to unbelief and rebellion. From out of the natural man comes the expression of the disease of sin and the wounding of shame. In Scripture this expression of fear is referred to as the flesh or the sin nature. From out of this place deep within the fear driven darkened soul, we view and interpret the experiences of our lives. This darkened perception then confirms our beliefs. From those beliefs we establish what is important to us, or the things that we deeply value.

Fear and shame are powerful forces within the soul of mankind, even in the soul of the believer in Christ. They can be truly devastating to our souls, and bring destruction to our lives and the lives of those we love. We need to look at how fear can keep us from experiencing the presence of God deeply within our souls. We need to look at how that fear leads to unbelief that can rob us of the abundant life God desires for us.

Carefully compare the *Original Nature* to the *Nature of Adam* graphic explanations.

	Original Nature	Nature of Adam
VIEW	Significance, value and provision is viewed through trust	The need for significance, value and provision is viewed through fear
BELIEF	God is in control, cares and will determine what my needs are and how they are met	**I** am in control and determine what my needs are and how they are met
PRIORITY	God and others are important to me	**Me**—I can have whatever I feel will meet my need
DRIVE	I will do what pleases God	I will please **myself**
BEHAVIOR	Compassion, Kindness, Gentleness, Love	Self-focus, Judgment, Control, Demand

The Struggle Within

Fear of God's judgment and punishment can be the source of our motivation to serve. The Bible tells us to fear God. But the fear that is referred to is a healthy fear of humble submission not a fear that causes us to run and hide in shame or drives us to serve out of duty instead of devotion. Fear and shame can even cause us to walk in false humility. Fear that is borne out of shame can keep us from knowing God as our loving Father.

Fear and unbelief can cause us to doubt God could use us or even would use us to serve Him and others. Fear and doubt can paralyze us and keep us from obeying His voice. Fear can cause us to hold tightly to our rights to direct our own way as we seek to manage our commitment to Him. Fear and unbelief can keep us in the tight grip of anxiety's bondage that constantly rob us of the wonder of living in abandonment to our God. The consequences of unbelief that come from fear and shame are truly staggering.

Review the *Meeting Our Need* graphic and note the following:

*   Instead of trusting God's provision for our needs, we seek possessions and pleasure.

*   Instead of knowing our value through His love and care, we seek value and approval from people and our abilities.

*   Instead of finding our significance through our position in relationship to God and His purposes, we seek position and power in this world and our own purposes to find meaning.

Fear that our basic needs will not be met causes us to doubt God.

1. Take a look at the passages that follow and describe what you learn about fear.

    a. I John 4:16-18

    _____

    _____

    _____

    b. Romans 8:12-17

    _____

    _____

    _____

    _____

Attributes of God

HOLY

God's justice and righteousness.

He is just and right in all He does.

SOVEREIGN

God's position and ability.

He is all powerful, completely

able and in total control.

RELATIONAL

God's love and goodness.

He loves unconditionally.

He always does what is in

our best interest for our good

and His glory.

So what is it we doubt about God? Why do we, in the quiet of our souls, wonder if God will come through for us the way we need? Why do we quietly whisper, "Where are You? Why aren't You doing something about this?"

There are three basic combinations of attributes of God that our fear driven soul will doubt. In the Christian community, we rarely share these doubts out loud. We would be seen as unspiritual. However the reality is most of us will struggle with at least one of these attributes of God at some time in our lives.

The three attributes we tend to question about God are:

• His justice and righteousness (Holy attributes)

• His position and ability to rule (Sovereign attributes)

• His love and goodness (Relational attributes)

Our doubt is seen in the form of questions that reveal our uncertainty in God's character.

Read the following scenarios.

A young mother dies of cancer or AIDS and leaves a young father to raise three little children. We're moved to say "it just isn't fair," but when thoughts of the fairness of life swirl through our minds, we are questioning God's justice. When we ask, "How could this be right?" we are questioning God's righteousness. Without saying a word out loud we are wondering deep within our souls if what God has done or allowed to happen was really right at all.

A child suffers through sexual abuse and we question how God could have allowed this to happen. When we ask, "Where was He? Couldn't He have stopped this?" we are questioning the power of God to rule with equity or at least for Him to rule as we think He should.

We find our bodies ravaged by a disease so painful we wonder at times where we will find the strength to take the next breath. We wonder how could God allow such pain? Doesn't He care? When we ask these kinds of questions, we question God's goodness and love.

Living In Fear

How significant are fear and unbelief to our relationship with God? Let's take a look at the Children of Israel and how they responded to the circumstances of their lives.

The Children of Israel were delivered from Egypt through the plagues. God delivered them and provided for them time after time in the wilderness. He provided water, manna, and quail. He went before them as a cloud by day and fire by night. He thundered from the mountain and poured out His wrath on them as they grumbled, complained and disobeyed. Yet over and over He protected and provided for them. Even though it wasn't always the way they desired, His provision was always more than they needed. When they finally came to the point of entering the Promised Land, Moses sent in twelve spies to see what it was like. Ten of the twelve came back angry and disgruntled because the land was rich and wonderful but full of danger and giants. They did not believe they could possess the land. They did not believe God could possess the land.

2.   Read Numbers 13:32-33. Explain what fear and unbelief did to them.

_____

_____

_____

_____

_____

In Numbers 13:33 the spies' report said: "We became like grasshoppers in our own sight and so we were in their sight." Fear gripped them, causing them to have a distorted view of themselves, of others, and of God.

3.   Write out below what it means to see one's self as a grasshopper.

_____

_____

_____

_____

The Children of Israel experienced the presence and power of God consistently in their lives. They knew His salvation, provision and protection, yet they kept responding in fear and unbelief.

4.   Read Numbers 14:1-4. How did they express the fear of their circumstances?

_____

_____

_____

_____

_____

5.   Read Hebrews 3:12-19. Summarize what you learn.

_____

_____

_____

_____

_____

6.   Which of the three attributes of God did the Children of Israel struggle to believe? Explain your answer.

_____

_____

_____

_____

_____

_____

_____

_____

_____

Because we are born with the nature of Adam it is natural to fear and view God with suspicion, however, as we mature in Him we will learn to trust Him more. We need to understand that maturity is a growth process. This means we need to deal with the fear and unbelief that is at the core of all the expressions of the flesh found within our souls – this is the journey to maturity in Christ.

A Look Inside

As we close this lesson, spend some time praying about what you have learned and answer the following questions.

1. How would you rate the level of your self-reliance that comes from fear, concerning the following basic needs?

   a. The need for your life to have meaning and purpose:

   trust God   0 – 1 – 2 – 3 – 4 – 5 – 6 – 7 – 8 – 9 – 10   **trust myself**

   Explain what brings you meaning and purpose.

   _____

   _____

   _____

   _____

   _____

   _____

   _____

   _____

   _____

   _____

   _____

   b. The need to be valued, loved and to belong:

   trust God   0 – 1 – 2 – 3 – 4 – 5 – 6 – 7 – 8 – 9 – 10   **trust myself**

   Explain what makes you feel valued.

   _____

   _____

   _____

   _____

   _____

   _____

   _____

   _____

   _____

   _____

   _____

c. The need to have your basic physical needs met:

trust God 0 – 1 – 2 – 3 – 4 – 5 – 6 – 7 – 8 – 9 – 10 **trust myself**

Explain your answer below.

_____

_____

_____

_____

_____

_____

_____

_____

_____

_____

2. Read II Corinthians 3:12-18. Remember that God has given us hope. His desire is for us to live in that hope. Finish this lesson remembering the hope you have in Christ. Describe the hope you should have.

_____

_____

_____

_____

_____

_____

_____

_____

_____

_____

_____

_____

_____

_____

_____

Understanding Our Condition
Shaped In Darkness   3

God's Intent

Because fear and shame have entered into the soul of man, it is important that we understand that God has other plans for us. He loves us far too much to leave us in the bondage of fear. He loves us far too much to leave us to ourselves. God wants to bring us back to the relationship of trust that we long for. God's desire is to restore us to that wondrous relationship of intimacy and unhindered oneness that we had in the Garden before sin marred our souls. He sent His perfect sinless Son to die a criminal's death to restore us to Himself.

> As for you, you were dead in your transgressions and sins, 2 in which you used to live when you followed the ways of this world and of the ruler of the kingdom of the air, the spirit who is now at work in those who are disobedient.
>
> — EPHESIANS 2:1-2 NIV

1. Read Ephesians 2:1-10 and answer the following questions.

   a. What was our condition and who was our governing power? (vs. 1-2)

   _____

   _____

   b. As a result of our condition what did we do? (vs. 3)

   _____

   _____

   c. What should have been the outcome? (vs. 3)

   _____

   _____

   d. What did God do? (vs. 5-6)

   _____

   _____

   e. Why did He act on our behalf? (vs. 4, 7, 10)

   _____

   _____

God has an eternal purpose for His creation and boundless love for His children. He has work for us to do. He will accomplish all that He desires in us as we walk in Him. We are His workmanship.

Remember, we have established that there are three parts to our salvation; justification, sanctification and glorification.

2. Read the following passages and record what you find.

    a.   Romans 8:28-30

    _____

    _____

    _____

    _____

    b.   Romans 12:1-2

    _____

    _____

    _____

    _____

In Romans 8:28-30 you can see the three elements of our salvation at work.

- We are called and **justified.** Justified is a judicial word and means to be given freedom from the penalty of sin. Our entire being is saved; spirit, soul and body – we are seen as holy by our God.

- We are **sanctified.** Cleansed and set apart for His purposes – freed from the power of sin as we are being made holy in all our motives and deeds. We are being conformed to the image of His Son.

- We will be **glorified.** When we die to this world and are set free from the flesh, we will be freed from the very presence of sin and the sin nature. We will share in the glory of the Son.

God has accomplished a complete work in His children. He is transforming us into the image of His Son. It takes time and we have to cooperate with Him. Philippians 1:6 says that the work He began in us He will finish! We can count on this fact; if we have been justified, we will be glorified.

The Condition of Man

God purposes to transform us into the image of His Son but at the very same time the enemy is determined to conform us after the pattern of this world (Romans 12:2). If we, as believers in Christ, live conformed to this world, Satan has won a major battle. In order to understand the work to which God is asking us to submit, we must understand what is happening inside our souls.

Before we come to Christ as our Savior and Lord we are held captive by the nature of Adam. We are not even able to act or think in ways other than Adam's nature. This means that every thought — no matter how noble, and no action — no matter how caring, is still in some way laced with self-oriented motivation that exists deep within our soul. The need for significance, value, and provision drive all that we do. In an effort to fulfill those self-oriented drives we will; pursue position in relationship to others, seek to gain value through relationships with people and personal achievement, and we will try to fulfill our fleshly appetites and basic needs with possessions and pleasures that gratify our desires.

Review the *Nature of Adam* graphic.

VIEW	The need for significance, value and provision is viewed through fear
BELIEF	**I** am in control and determine what my needs are and how they are met
PRIORITY	**Me**–I can have whatever I feel will meet my need
DRIVE	I will please **myself**
BEHAVIOR	Self-focus, Judgment, Control, Demand I seek: Power & Position, People & Performance, and Possessions & Pleasure

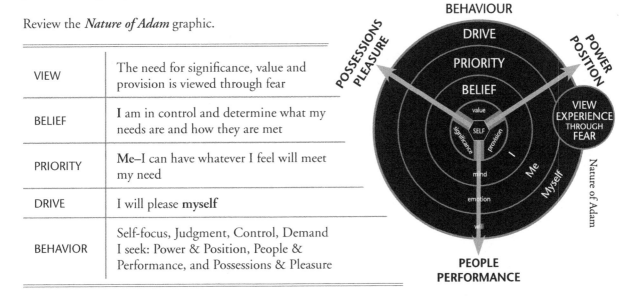

To understand this more clearly, let's look again at our souls.

This time let's look at what has happened to our souls through Adam's sin. We will then see how the condition of our fearful soul is viewed through the experiences of our lives to create a way of responding to people and to God that is not an expression of love, but an expression of the old man or natural man.

When we are born into this world, according to Romans 5, we have a soul nature that follows after the ways of Adam. It is diseased like Adam's soul. Because of this, it is bent towards independence, rebellion, self-preservation, and self-satisfaction. This is the very definition of sin and is completely contrary to the divine nature God desires for us. It is filled with fear that our need will not be met. We fear we will not be significant, loved and valued, or satisfied. Because of Adam, man chooses to satisfy these needs on his own and because it is impossible to do so, he lives in fear constantly striving to meet his own need.

1. Read the following passages and fill in the chart. Note that not every passage addresses every question, so some parts of the chart will remain blank.

Where does the natural man come from?	What is the character of the natural man? What is it like?	How is the nature expressed? What does it do?
Romans 5:18-19		
Galatians 5:16-23		
I Corinthians 2:14		

Scripture tells us we are born into sin. This means the nature within us at birth will always be driven and motivated by two primary things — rebellion and shame — that are derived from fear that we will not have our needs met. When we have the Spirit within us our internal condition will change. We are given the ability to choose to follow after the ways of the flesh or the ways of the Spirit.

There is a war going on over the soul of man, even the soul of the believer in Christ. Satan is intent on distorting the truth and defeating the work of the Spirit in the life of the believer in Christ. He does this through exploiting the needs within man, which fuels his drives to meet his need as seems best to him.

Review the *The Struggle Within* graphic. You can see that fear can drive us to meet our inner need our own way. The war between the flesh and the Spirit is very much alive keeping us from doing what we know God desires.

In Colossians, Paul seems to have two basic categories that are expressions of the natural man.

2. From the passages below, list the things that are expressed by the "old self."

   a. Colossians 3:5-7

   _____

   _____

   _____

   _____

   _____

DRIVE

PRIORITY

BELIEF

POSSESSIONS PLEASURE

POWER POSITION

VIEW EXPERIENCE THROUGH TRUST

VIEW EXPERIENCE THROUGH FEAR

value

GOD

significance · provision

humility · pride

gratitude · entitlement

devotion · idolatry

mind

emotion

will

The Struggle Within

PEOPLE PERFORMANCE

   b. Colossians 3:8-9

   _____

   _____

   _____

   _____

   _____

   _____

   _____

We need to be sure we understand the terminology used by New Testament writers. Throughout Paul's writings we see the terms "the old man," "our old sinful selves" and the "natural man." These terms refer to the person we were before we received forgiveness and before we had the Holy Spirit within us. It refers to the person we were, when our lives were completely governed by the sinful nature we inherited from Adam (Romans 5). The terms "the sinful nature" and "the flesh" refer to the expression of the nature we received from Adam. The "inner man" refers to the place within us where both the soul and the spirit of man exist.

When Satan tempted Eve in the Garden, he exploited her God given need. He introduced the idea that the tree God had said not to eat from was not bad, but actually good.

3. Read Genesis 3:4-7. Note the three ways the tree of knowledge was good.

   _____

   _____

   _____

Terms

OLD MAN, SINFUL SELVES, NATURAL MAN

Who we were before justification.

SINFUL NATURE, THE FLESH

The nature we received from Adam.

INNER MAN

The place within us where both the soul and spirit of man exist.

3 : Shaped in Darkness

Man's soul has been invaded by the sinful nature and this nature's only concern is what it can get for itself. We can categorize the expression of the sinful nature into three basic types:

- **Physical:** The need to satisfy our physical appetites (the woman saw that the tree was good for food).

- **Emotional:** The need to have what brings us pleasure; this is also called idolatry or greed (it was a delight to the eyes).

- **Spiritual:** The need to know that our lives have meaning and we have a significant place in the order of things. We need to know and be known. When we demand this place of position and knowledge apart from God and how He created us, it is pride (it was good to make one wise).

Because we are motivated to meet our own needs, we are in conflict with God's desire for how we should have those needs met. Our entire lives center on gaining satisfaction any way we can apart from God. This is rebellion and independence. And shame causes us to protect our souls against the wounding of being devalued in the eyes of others.

In Colossians 3:5-7 Paul lists expressions of the need to satisfy the passions of our flesh that fall under the three categories listed from Genesis 3:4-5. In Colossians 3:8-9 we see expressions of the need to cover our shame. Remember the definition of shame is a disfigured soul, which has been disgraced or diminished in value.

- **Physical expression:** Immorality, impurity, sensuality, drunkenness, carousing

- **Emotional (soul) expressions:** Enmities, strife, jealousy, anger, envying, etc.

- **Spiritual expressions:** Sorcery, idolatry, pride, entitlement

In our modern vernacular the terms we have substituted for the flesh and its expressions are "survival mechanisms." We use these survival mechanisms or expressions of the flesh to protect ourselves from the devaluing brought on by shame, and to protect our rights to the expressions of rebellion and independence; we reserve the right to protect and satisfy our souls.

The Struggle Within

There are three arenas of life that shape our belief and deeply affect our soul's ability to respond in love to God and man as He desires: significant relationships, life circumstances, and sin and shame.

These three arenas, combined with the darkened fear-driven soul of man, cause us to believe that God cannot or will not satisfy our needs. As a result we develop ways of responding to others and even to God to try to protect and satisfy our soul, so we feel safe from hurt and suffering. These survival mechanisms may seem to serve us well, but will always cause us to respond to life, people, and God in ways other than what God desires.

Why does it seem the anger that ruled our lives before we began this journey with Christ still reigns in our marriages? Why are we still struggling to feel loved or known or seen by others? Why do we still feel anxiety or fear in relationships or in our financial situations? Why do we still hunger to belong or hunger for a relationship that is truly satisfying? If we ask these questions out loud we will often be told we just don't have enough faith. We learn to just keep our inner hunger and hurt to ourselves, put on a smile, and wonder what is wrong with us or maybe even what is wrong with God. Some of us will serve more or study more, thinking that someday we may be able to do enough to fill the longing within us; others will just walk away.

1.   Read Matthew 23:23-28 and summarize what you learn.

_____

_____

_____

In order to experience all Christ has promised in this abundant life, we must cooperate with Him to clean the inside of the cup. In order to do that, we must take an honest look inside. We must see how our souls have been affected by the relationships and circumstances we have experienced in life and how we naturally respond to them apart from God. We carry much of this "natural" behavior into our new life with Christ and we find the best we can do is behavior modification, much like the Scribes and Pharisees of Jesus' day. We still struggle to love our parents or that older sibling that hurt us so badly. We still struggle with jealousy. We still slander or gossip. We still feel the need to be seen and approved of by others, so we demand our way at church and fight for positions in ministries. We still hunger for more in our marriages. Only the outside has been changed.

Read the following article written by Diana Berns and prayerfully reflect on its meaning.

Today I read a post stating: "Satan has no power."

While this is true in some sense, the statement is incomplete. When I look around and evaluate the spiritual condition of those around me, I don't have to look further than my immediate family to realize that sin indeed has devastating effects. In all reality I don't need to look further than myself to see how Satan (or those working in his service) have tricked me into thinking things that are untrue. The "father of lies" is a master of deceit. He doesn't give you a bold faced lie to ponder. The thoughts come as questions. Relentless questions. Questions that cause me to doubt what I know is true. This is the power he holds. It's a mental game and quite effective. His undetected invasion of our thoughts incubates the unbelief in our souls. Because of our unique design and need for value, and significance we are ripe and ready to produce a reaction that will inflict damage on others as Satan exploits our weakness.

It is true that when we are born into a spiritual relationship with God, sin is rendered powerless. So if sin is rendered powerless how or why do I feel defeated? Why are there so many days when victory feels far off. What is the power that Satan has? We need to understand the battle tactics he uses to win the affections of our soul. Satan is not concerned with our public worship of him. His objective is to keep us from receiving and living in the power God gives His children. If he can stunt our progress in understanding the knowledge of God he has achieved quite a victory.

Satan is actually a behavior specialist. If we can look at how we have been shaped by the patterns of this world - those things we have had no control over - it may give us a way to see how the arch-enemy of God has been at work long before we arrived on the battle field. Because he has the advantage of observing human behavior throughout the centuries, we cannot underestimate his ability to anticipate and exploit. This is a powerful weapon.

With the Spirit of God in us, He gives us the strength (power) to overcome the enemy's attacks. We even get to participate in the battle and share the glory of God as He celebrates these victories with us. Sin is indeed rendered powerless as we cut off the avenues in our thinking that react to Satan's tactics and choose to believe the hope in the very visible unseen reality of God. (Faith)

Understanding how Satan uses our experiences against us will cause us to look to our Creator to see His purpose in allowing the struggles that cause so much pain. It is truly a wondrous plan. Scripture tells us that Christ is seen in our weakness. These moments of weakness, when our foe waits for the same reaction he has grown to expect; when we respond in a way that is contrary to our natural tendencies, people notice. These moments give us opportunity to speak of the hope we have.

So it is true: Satan has no power, other than the power we give him. Don't be deceived into underestimating the enemy of God.

A Look Inside

Spend time reflecting on what your soul was like before you came to faith in Christ.

1. List the passions and motivations that may have controlled or driven you.

_____

_____

_____

_____

_____

_____

2. Describe how you respond to people in high stress situations or when you have been unjustly accused or rejected by someone you love.

_____

_____

_____

_____

_____

_____

3. Do any of the past motivations still govern your actions? Explain

_____

_____

_____

_____

_____

4. Do you still struggle with uncontrolled appetites (whether sexual or food oriented)?

_____

_____

_____

_____

3 : Shaped in Darkness

5. Do you hunger for the approval of man?

_____

_____

_____

_____

_____

_____

When we look at Romans 12 "do not be conformed by the patterns of this world but be transformed" we can see that we are shaped from external conditions – patterns of our families, culture and economics status.

God's desire is for you to experience Him in all of His fullness. Ask Him for His wisdom and strength as together you evaluate your relationship. Allow Him to help you see what prevents you from knowing and loving Him as He desires.

In this section "Shaping Our View," we will look at the lenses that have shaped our soul, distorting our view of God and man. We live in the world and have been influenced by all that we have experienced. Our experiences can help us evaluate why we react and respond to God and others as we do. The intent is not to dig up old wounds or blame others for what we have become, but to give us understanding. We will seek to discover what has shaped us. We will look at the ways we have reacted that do not reflect the changed nature He desires. We need to allow His Spirit to shine His Light in us – changing us from the inside out.

Shaping Our View
Significant Relationships   *4*

God's Intent

Man is not a well thought out experiment of some higher intelligence. He isn't the result of some random coming together of molecules or atoms at just the right time in just the right environment. He did not accidently evolve over eons of time to become a relational sentient being. A relational loving God created us and intended us to experience life and love through relationship.

> 20 "My prayer is not for them alone. I pray also for those who will believe in me through their message, 21 that all of them may be one, Father, just as you are in me and I am in you. May they also be in us so that the world may believe that you have sent me.
>
> — JOHN 17:20-21 NIV

In John 17 we see that God, in His being, is a Triune God and exists in a community of complete unity and love within the Godhead. When He created us in His image, He created us to experience this same love and unity that is intrinsic to the Godhead. He put us in families to help us understand what it means to live outside of our self-oriented need. We were created by God to find fulfillment of our core needs through a relationship with Him and within the family experience.

As you look at the *God's Design* graphic note that God designed man to experience significance, value, and physical provision through both relationship with Him and with each other.

The foundation of family is crucial to our understanding and experience of our loving heavenly Father. Family as a community and the individual significant relationships that exist within the family unit are foundational to God's purpose and design for man.

1. Read Ephesians 5:21-31.

    a. Describe the love the husband is to have for the wife.

    _____

    _____

    _____

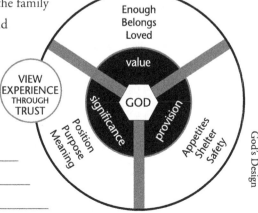

_____

_____

b.   Describe the love the wife is to have for the husband.

_____

_____

c.   Describe the relationship we are to have with Christ.

_____

_____

The purpose of this study is not to delve deeply into the different relationships within the family and the way they are to be experienced. However, we can know that within the intimacy of the marriage relationship, God gives us a picture of the relationship He desires to have with us. This relationship is to be based on the principles of identification, devotion, affection, and a binding covenant commitment.

2.   Read the following passages and record how your earthly and heavenly father compare.

a.   Romans 8:15

_____

_____

b.   Matthew 6:26, 32

_____

_____

c.   Luke 6:36

_____

_____

We can also see, within the father–child relationship, God's intent for us is to experience Him as our heavenly Father (1 John 3:1). We can know that God longs to delight in His children. He longs to be with us in a communion of love. He desires to care for us, protect us and provide for us in ways that only He can.

God has designed us for relationship; the family is intended to be God's way of showing us what a relationship with Him is to be like. Within relationships, both in the family and with God, we are designed to experience spiritual significance, value, and belonging and have our physical needs met.

The Condition of Man

Because of what sin has done to the soul of man, to be valued by others is the greatest of all emotional needs. Some of the most daunting psychological disorders can be traced back to times in childhood when children were not valued well or not valued at all. Most of us have heard about studies done on children from orphanages that have had little to no nurturing from infancy, and the seemingly irreversible damage to those children's ability to ever give or receive love.

The need to be significant, valued, and provided for drives every relationship. We need to know somebody somewhere thinks we are worth loving. We need to know somebody believes that what is inside of us is worth standing for — even worth fighting for — somehow even worth dying for. The need to be significant and valued is a part of everything we do, so much so, that we often do not even recognize how it affects us. Remember, the experience of these things is not wrong. God designed us to experience these things for the express purpose of driving us to Him. However, when they do not find their home in Him, we are left with a longing that cannot be filled.

We need to see how what went wrong in the Garden impacts our ability to relate to God and others as He intends.

Surviving Relationships

Remember, because of Adam's sin, we are born with a nature that seeks to have its core needs met above all else. We are born self-focused. We are by nature self-oriented, suspicious and insecure. This innate fear that we will not have our needs met affects our view of all relationships. Even when our families meet our needs well, we bring that expectation into other relationships and become disappointed when what we have come to expect is not given. When our significant relationships fail us, another layer of fear is added to distort our view of God and others as our belief is confirmed that we will need to take care of our need on our own. Our family may applaud our ability to take care of ourselves, which then solidifies our determination to be self-reliant and independent.

Let's take a look at how we process the experience of relational interaction within the soul. Review the *Nature of Adam* graphic.

Several things happen in the soul almost simultaneously. Our minds make decisions based on our perception of an experience – even referring to a past similar experience – which then attaches an emotional response to our perception. The emotion we attach to the experience will cause us to make a decision about what to do with what we have perceived. This decision happens in our will. Once our mind is made up about what has happened and how we feel about it, then we decide how we will react. This all happens internally before any action or behavior is seen.

Jacob and Esau

Significant family relationships play a major part in forming our souls. How our parents and those close to us have loved us imprints a sense of value and belonging into our souls. When those relationships fail to meet our need, we find ourselves struggling to find value within ourselves. The resulting wounds penetrate our soul, leaving us with a pain and emptiness we will do anything to relieve. We create survival mechanisms around our souls, strengthening our flesh and creating a way of living that is rooted in the natural man. We make the decision, either consciously or subconsciously, to do anything to avoid the pain of being devalued or insignificant. The walls around our soul go up and the self-protection grows.

1. Read Genesis 25:19-34; Genesis 27:1-45 and summarize the story.

_____

_____

_____

_____

_____

2. Reflect on the family dynamics. Record how the parents' relationships with each of these men affected their nature and the way they learned to relate to others.

_____

_____

_____

_____

_____

It is easy to see from scripture that the parent-child relationship is crucial in forming our inner man, our ability to relate to others, and to love others well. Throughout scripture we can see the devastating effects upon the soul when children were not loved well by their parents, whether through neglect, abandonment, favoritism, or unrealistic expectations. Eli the priest failed to discipline his sons and they became evil, greedy priests who took advantage of God's people (I Samuel 2:22-34). Jacob learned to show favoritism from his parents in the story we read above, and he in turn favored Joseph. This caused Joseph to become spoiled which caused all kinds of family problems (Genesis 37:3-4). David failed to deal with his boys, resulting in incest and murder amongst his children (2 Samuel 13).

The Struggle Within

Where does this need for value come from? Without a doubt it is a part of our inner man, but what has happened to cause it to become such a compelling drive within us?

When Adam and Eve sinned, they suddenly lost sight of their place in creation and a huge wall of guilt and shame stood between them and God. They turned to fig leaves to hide their shame and became disappointed in each other, themselves, and God. Blame, expectations and demands became a part of their lives and from that time on man has had to constantly work to establish his position as he seeks his place in this world.

What went wrong then and what goes wrong in us now? We need to go back even before Eve sinned and look at the lies spoken into her life by Satan.

There are some very significant things we can discern about the nature of mankind and the way God has created us by looking into the Scriptures directly preceding the fall of man. The first thing we note is that man can be easily persuaded to doubt his own sense of value and his place and purpose in God's design.

1. Read and summarize Genesis 3:1-7.

    _____

    _____

    _____

    _____

    _____

Right away we can see that Satan is persuading Eve to re-evaluate God's opinion of her. Satan implies that God is not looking out for her best interest. He implies that God does not value her place in the scheme of things enough to take care of them— they will need to make their own way. God should value them more. Satan leads them to believe that God is withholding something from them. He causes Eve to doubt God's loving intent.

Before sin was ever conceived in the hearts of man, Satan spoke lies. He spoke lies into the soul of man about how God valued the man and woman. Eve allowed those lies to turn her gaze away from Living God and look to her own understanding. Her response to the lies about her value to God and His care for her moves her to choose to sin.

2. Read Genesis 3:16. Note how her choice affected her relationship with her husband.

    _____

    _____

    _____

From this moment on she will work and position herself, against her husband and all other relationships, for what she feels is her rightful place in this world. And man will blame woman for his weaknesses and failure in an effort to gain back his sense of worth.

The spoken word is the most powerful force in existence. The spoken word of God created all that exists. The spoken lies of Satan turned the eyes of man away from Living God to gaze upon anything that might bring value to his own life or make him have value in the eyes of others.

There have been things spoken into your life by others that have affected your view of God and others. You may have survived a childhood where someone spoke into your life verbally or they may have spoken volumes through their actions; neglect, abandonment, smothering or pressure to succeed. Either way, we are told all kinds of things that shape our view and ultimately our nature. They can be as simple as "well you may be smart and educated, but when it comes to daily life you don't know anything," or, "It is a good thing you are a hard worker because you aren't going to make it with your brains," or even, "It's a good thing you're beautiful because personality and brains passed you by." Stupid, lazy, ugly, fat, skinny, worthless – all become words imprinted into our souls, causing us to assume a false identity, shaping our view and ultimately our souls in ways God never intended. We will either choose to believe them or we will spend our lives seeking to prove them wrong.

Whatever was spoken, your soul was molded and shaped contrary to the way God originally created you. Listening to those lies will ultimately lead to sin. We will end up with our gaze turned away from our God as we seek to have our need for worth satisfied somewhere else.

In the *Significant Relationships* graphic you can see that significant relationships are like a lens over our soul that distorts our ability to see God and others clearly. This distortion contributes to the fear that our need will not be met and strengthens the resolve of our belief.

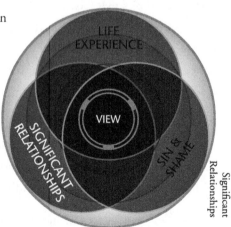

How do we find our way to the place where we are at peace with exactly how God created us? How do we get to a place where we are not living in pride, constantly lifting our position above others – where we are not always seeking approval and value? God has made a way back to Him. We need to consider how we have been shaped by our significant relationships and see what we have settled for to meet the need God placed inside of us.

A Look Inside

As we seek to understand the ways significant relationships have shaped our view, keep in mind that our natural tendency is to evaluate relationships based on our need for significance, value and provision: determining if and how those needs will be met.

Remember God's intent for families is to use the relational environment to help meet our needs. We aren't looking to see what is wrong with our families and assign blame or open old wounds. What we desire is that we recognize that families alone cannot give us all we need and many fall far short – even as we fall short.

Though many have experienced very positive significant relationships, there is no environment that is perfect. Even in the best family environments there are both positive and negative impacts. Consider the following scenarios.

Scenario 1

When a father is a rigid or even abusive disciplinarian, a child will develop behaviors that protect him from the possible consequences of failure. His core need for significance and value is exposed by the relational interaction causing him to believe that if he fails he is not valued. An emotional response attached to the possibility of failure will cause him to determine how he will react. This decision will be evident in any number of behaviors as he seeks to protect his soul from being devalued and seen as insignificant.

- He may be filled with anxiety and decide he must not fail no matter what the cost. Fear of failure drives him to decide that lying or cheating are viable options.

- He may be filled with resignation because he knows he will fail, so he doesn't try.

- He may learn that success means value, so he pours himself into his work and becomes a perfectionist, because he is determined to please at any cost.

Scenario 2

It is not just the difficult relationships that shape our perspective and impact our souls. We can have very loving and positive family relationships that shape our perspective in ways that God does not desire. A young girl might be loved well by her father. He may treat her like a princess and develop a very rich relationship with her. However when she grows into a woman she may find relationships with men difficult.

- She may have difficulty finding anyone ever good enough to replace her father. She may unjustly compare the two men making her husband feel he can never be good enough for her. She may criticize him in public hoping to shame him into appropriate behavior or use stabbing criticism in private as she demands her needs be met.

4 : Significant Relationships

47

- She may find it difficult to shift her loyalty from her father to her husband. When difficulties arise she may find herself running to her father for advise instead of working through them with her husband.

- If she was well cared for financially she may become caustic and critical, putting constant pressure on her husband to meet the standard of living she had always known. She may choose to spend money unwisely not caring about the pressure it puts on the family and her husband.

1. What significant relationship had the most impact on you coming to faith in Christ? This can be either a positive impact or negative. Explain how?

_____

_____

_____

_____

_____

_____

_____

_____

_____

2. List below the significant relationships in your life that have impacted your soul the most and explain how.

_____

_____

_____

_____

_____

_____

_____

_____

3. What was the message you received about yourself from each of the relationships you listed? Have you chosen to believe the message (stated verbally or implied through actions) or determined to prove them wrong? Explain.

_____

_____

_____

_____
_____
_____
_____
_____
_____
_____

4. What decisions have you made in response to the messages received through each of these relationships?

_____
_____
_____
_____
_____
_____
_____
_____

5. Explain how these decisions impact your ability to give love and receive the love of others and from God.

_____
_____
_____
_____
_____
_____
_____

6. Can you identify how these relationships have caused you to seek to have your need for significance, value and provision met through position, power, people, performance, possessions or pleasure? Be specific.

_____
_____
_____
_____
_____
_____

7. How do you believe this impacts your relationship with God?

_____

_____

_____

_____

_____

_____

_____

_____

_____

_____

As you finish this lesson, remember that God has a plan for you to thrive in relationships. He longs to give you every opportunity to bring you to a place where you can experience both Him and others in deep, meaningful, loving relationships. He longs to satisfy the deep need in your soul in a way that will bring Him honor. Our recognition of our need for Him is part of His loving process.

Shaping Our View
Life Experience 5

God's Intent

When God placed man in the Garden, He gave him an abundant life. Man was placed in a lush garden that was watered by springs and fountains that came up from the ground. There were trees and animals in abundance and more than enough food. He had spiritual significance because he had an eternal purpose to tend the Garden, be fruitful and multiply, and subdue the earth. God walked with him and talked with him in the cool of the evening. His very presence gave man value and spiritual significance. God gave man a companion to share his life with. God gave man a place to be – a connection to the land. He gave him a place to belong. And finally God gave circumstances in which to live where there was no pain or suffering; there was no death. Suffering and strife only came into existence after sin entered. Man lived an abundant life at peace with God, his wife, and his environment. His life circumstances were complete and perfect. All his needs were completely satisfied.

> ⁸ Now the Lord God had planted a garden in the east, in Eden; and there he put the man he had formed. ⁹ The Lord God made all kinds of trees grow out of the ground—trees that were pleasing to the eye and good for food.
>
> — GENESIS 2:8-9 NIV

Since Adam sinned, God has been calling man back to the Garden. Only now, the Garden symbolizes the place within the soul of man where His Spirit dwells in the believer in Jesus Christ. Now, since sin entered the world, we need to see what God is purposing and bringing about through man's life experiences.

1. Read the following passages and record what God desires for us.

   a.   Isaiah 61:1-4

   _____

   _____

   _____

   _____

   _____

b. John 10:7-10

(Note that the word "life" in the Greek is referring to spiritual life.)

_____

_____

_____

_____

c. Romans 8:28-30

_____

_____

_____

_____

_____

Review the *God's Design* graphic and remember that God desires that we trust Him completely in all arenas of our need.

God still desires physical abundance for His children, however, because sin has entered the lives of all mankind, our spiritual and soul condition takes precedence over our temporal and physical need. His desire is that we trust Him with how He chooses care for us.

2. Study the following passages and record what God's priorities are for us through life circumstances.

a. I John 2:15-17

_____

_____

_____

_____

b. II Corinthians 4:16-18

_____

_____

_____

_____

c. Romans 2:28-29

_____

_____

_____

God desires spiritual abundance in the life of the believer in Christ. It is His number one priority. He longs for us to live in trusting abandon through the circumstances of this life. When we do, the garden of our soul will flourish for all to see.

The Condition of Man

There are many things that shape our soul; culture, social status, birth order and a host of other circumstances and experiences. Some of those things are neither good or bad, they just are. Experiences of life and circumstances outside of our control shape our perception of God and others. Life happens, and it serves up a daily offering that ranges from the ordinary routine of daily living to deep and profound trauma. Each circumstance or experience has the potential to expose the condition of our soul. With each circumstance we face, we have the option of choosing to trust that a loving God has allowed it and respond from the strength He provides or fall back into our natural pattern of response, strengthening our inner resolve and the survival mechanisms we have developed. Others will see our new nature – God's divine nature – or the old nature of Adam we have learned to rely on.

So where do these survival mechanisms that protect our souls come from? How are they formed and strengthened within us? How is our view shaped, that forms our beliefs, and drives our behaviors in ways that are not according to the desires of God?

Review the *Nature of Adam* graphic.

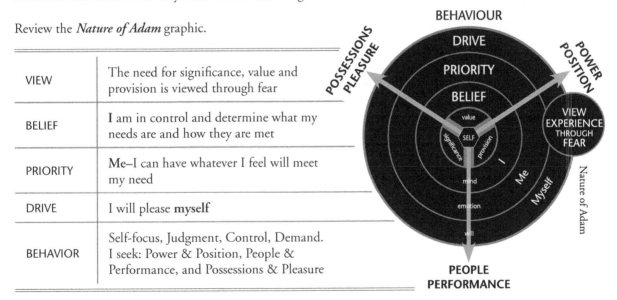

VIEW	The need for significance, value and provision is viewed through fear
BELIEF	**I** am in control and determine what my needs are and how they are met
PRIORITY	**Me**–I can have whatever I feel will meet my need
DRIVE	I will please **myself**
BEHAVIOR	Self-focus, Judgment, Control, Demand. I seek: Power & Position, People & Performance, and Possessions & Pleasure

Again as we look at this graphic, we need to remember how our souls naturally process our life experiences. Before Christ, we viewed all of life through a lens of fear. The fear we received from Adam perceives all circumstances based on how those circumstances will affect our core needs for significance, value, and provision. As we experience life, our view is continuously impacted which shapes our beliefs. We then determine what is important to us, attaching an emotional response to what we decide to do.

Abram and Sarai (Abraham and Sarah)

1. Read the scripture below and note the significant circumstance of Sarai and Abram's life. Sarai and Abram's names were later changed to Sarah and Abraham.

    a.   Genesis 11:30

    _____

The writer of Genesis felt it necessary to the rest of Abraham's story to include this vital piece of information. Therefore we can assume it has great bearing on Abraham's future and his actions.

It is significant to understand how important these circumstances are in the life of Abraham. Being able to have a child was deeply important to life in biblical times. People in those times believed they would gain a level of immortality through their offspring. Children were needed to pass down the family name and inheritance. The number of children a woman was able to bear, especially male children, often defined her value in society. Children helped with the family estate and passed down the family's position within the community. They were crucial to the social and economic well-being of the family. Children, especially the male children, were considered evidence of God's favor or blessing.

2. Read the following passages. Summarize how Abraham responded to each set of circumstances.

    a.   Genesis 12:1-5. Note the promises God made to him.

    _____

    _____

    _____

    _____

    b.   Genesis 12:10-20

    _____

    _____

    _____

    _____

    c.   Genesis 15:1-6. Note the promise God gave.

    _____

    _____

    _____

    _____

    d.   Genesis 16:1-6, 15

_____

_____

_____

_____

    e.   Genesis 20:1-7

_____

_____

_____

_____

There is a pattern of response Abraham seemed to fall into as he found himself dealing with the difficult situations in life.

3.   Describe that response below.

_____

_____

_____

_____

_____

_____

As Abraham's life story shows, there came a time when he believed God, and God called him righteous. This means in God's eyes Abraham would no longer be judged by his actions but by his faith. God accepted him in a covenant relationship before he was proven faithful.

Even with this acceptance by God, and God's promises and presence, Abraham still tried to find his own way through life circumstances. When he couldn't see what God was doing or how God was going to accomplish what He had promised, Abraham always had a plan. He was deeply concerned with self-protection and satisfaction.

Can you see how the lack of trust in God's provision was deeply woven into Abraham's soul? God had not given him children and he was getting old. Then God promised him a child but Abraham could not see how God was going to come through since he and Sarah were so old. It didn't matter how many times God spoke personally to him. The visible evidence of God's provision and blessing was not there in the form of a son. Abraham always seemed to have a backup plan, right up until the end of his life, when God asked him to sacrifice the son of promise, his only son, Isaac (Genesis 22).

The Consequences of Self-Protection

Often, we do not see the consequences imposed on others when we respond to life from our distorted view. Lives are deeply affected and even broken because of the choices we make when we are driven by self-protection. As we consider the circumstances of our lives, we can break these into two categories.

The first includes the events of life that are beyond our control or maybe we have initiated ourselves through choices we have made. The other includes the things that others have done to us – when we have been sinned against. The sin committed against us will shape and mold our soul. Sin brings disease and wounding and the effects of sin are devastating. Take another look at the story of Abraham and Sarah. You will see how the consequences of Abraham's self-protection impacted generations to come as he and Sarah committed a devastating sin against others.

4. Read Genesis 21:2-3, 9-21 and identify the consequences of Abraham's actions in the lives of others.

_____

_____

_____

_____

Hagar and her son Ishmael suffered through banishment and rejection. Ishmael went on to become one of the forefathers of the Arab Nation, which has been at war with Israel ever since.

Some of us hold on to the wounds we get from others like a treasure. We believe that because of what was done to us we are entitled to the defense mechanisms that bring us comfort and security. How could they be sin when they are all that has stood between our complete shattering and us? We cling to these things, which, keep us from experiencing the abundance of Christ's love in our lives, and believe if God had not wanted us this way He would not have allowed this to happen in the first place. Now who we are in our flesh seems to be His fault.

Many times as we seek to survive life, we develop what we believe are admirable survival mechanisms, which even become a source of pride. When we are survivors of life we often become very resourceful and self-sufficient. Independence and capability become our strengths, yet these very things can prevent us from total dependency on God. A self-sufficient person cannot know what it means to be totally abandoned or surrendered to God. As we live from out of our distorted view, we damage our ability to give and receive love from God and from those around us.

Review the *God's Design* and *The Struggle Within* graphics and note how we as believers in Christ can find ourselves pursuing the wrong things as we try to meet our need on our own.

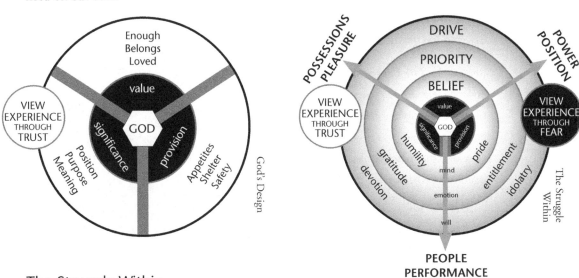

The Struggle Within

Even as believers in Christ, the expression of the flesh in our lives is very real. Many of the things that governed and drove us before we placed our faith in Jesus Christ have not been changed at all. For many of us, most of the expressions of our natural man have just been modified to fit into our cleaned up Christian appearance. These are behavior modifications, and aside from the fact they are not true change, they are often just our own efforts to protect souls filled with need and shame.

Think about the biggest sources of stress, pain, and disappointment in your life and specifically think about the times these have seemed overwhelming (perhaps you are in the midst of one of these times even now). How do you respond and how do you pray in these times?

Consider these questions:

- Do you ask again and again, "Why is this happening to me?"

- Do you find yourself scrambling to control the pieces of your stressed out life as work and family begin to fall apart?

- Do you repeat "the Christian phrases" to yourself over and over, trying to convince yourself God is protecting you or His love is enough, but you still feel empty, alone, abandoned and isolated or wounded?

- Do you tell yourself to just put on the smile and keep going, hoping it will all work out, all the while building walls of fear and shame around your soul?

- Do you isolate and withdraw; become cold or harsh?

- Do you work harder, serving more as you seek to please others?

All of these reactions and other kinds of survival mechanisms are reasonable from any human perspective. However they are nothing more than behaviors designed to protect our souls from the pain we have experienced in this life. How you feel and respond inside will tell you how deeply the roots of self-protection have wound down into the core of your soul.

Review the *Life Experience* graphic and note how the lens of life experience is added to lens of significant relationships. Now both of these arenas are added to our view of either fear or trust, which in turn establishes what we believe about life, others, and God.

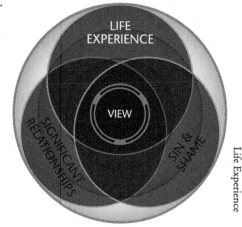

God's Design for Suffering

As hard as it may be to understand, God has a purpose for every hardship we experience in life. If He cannot use them for our good and His glory, He would not allow them to happen to us (Romans 8:28-29). God did not give Abraham a son until "his body was as good as dead" (Hebrews 11:12) so He could be glorified and the world would know that Jehovah God is a God of the impossible. He waited to give Abraham a son to prove Abraham's faith and make it strong – God had work to do on Abraham's soul. God needed to transform this sometimes weak and doubting man into a man of great faith so he could be the father of a great nation. God's design for this man's life was to bring about the salvation of all mankind through his descendants.

1. Read the passages below. List the reasons for the suffering we experience.

    a. Romans 5:3-5

    _____

    _____

    _____

    b. Philippians 3:7-8

    _____

    _____

    _____

    c. Romans 8:16-17

    _____

    _____

Our wounded and diseased soul, shaped like the Nature of Adam, will take the difficult experiences of life and use them to form survival mechanisms to insulate us from pain and help us get what we think will satisfy our need. The Spirit of Living God desires to use these same experiences to transform us into the image of His Son Jesus Christ as we learn to trust Him.

A Look Inside

Anyone reading these words has asked God "why" during some hard time in life. Most of us come running to God looking for Him to give us peace in the midst of our storm – but what if it was not peace we sought, but He who is peace? What if we quit seeking God for soul satisfaction and sought Him just because He is God and is calling us to Himself? What if we didn't live for God so we could get something from Him? What if we lived for Him because we had experienced Him? Could the experience of loving Him with an open and abandoned soul be enough?

As we look inside our soul, we are seeking to understand the ways that life experiences and circumstances have shaped our view. Remember that our natural tendency is to determine whether something is good or bad based on how the experience affected us. It is important for us to ask the Creator of our soul to show us what He would like us to see. Do not skim over this part or take it lightly. Spend some time reflecting on your life and answer the following questions. This is not an academic exercise.

1. List below on the time line the circumstances and life experiences you believe have shaped you the most. Below the time line explain how. (Examples of these would be the loss of a loved one, birth order or number of siblings, sickness or disease, loss of a job, work environment, being wealthy or poor, or a constant uprooting of your life through family moves.) Be sure to include when you came to faith in Christ and what circumstances surrounded that event.

Birth   Today

I--I

2. List below the ways you respond in difficult situations as a result of the things you listed on the time line. (What do they bring out in you? How do you react to stress, trauma, rejection or not getting your way? Not just in the immediacy, but as time goes on. These are your survival mechanisms.)

Survival Mechanisms

withdraw,

hide,

run,

lie,

cheat,

cover up,

ignore,

laugh,

smile,

pretend,

get angry,

act out,

plan,

manipulate,

go to vices,

etc...

_____

_____

_____

_____

_____

_____

_____

_____

_____

_____

_____

3. What have these circumstances or experiences caused you to believe about yourself, God and others?

_____

_____

_____

_____

_____

_____

_____

_____

4. This next question can be the hardest to answer for many reasons. You will need to take a very hard look at those around you and the decisions you make. What are the consequences of the survival mechanisms you rely on? Who do they affect and how?

_____

_____

_____
_____
_____
_____
_____
_____
_____
_____

5.   How do these mechanisms affect your relationship with God and others?

_____
_____
_____
_____
_____
_____
_____
_____
_____
_____
_____
_____
_____
_____
_____
_____
_____
_____

As we finish this session remember that God's work of transformation takes time. Do not be discouraged at how deeply the self-protection and survival mechanisms run through your soul. God's desire for you is for your good and His glory. He will not let you go and will not stop working on you until He sees His Son reflected in the way you live and love. Be encouraged and know He is working.

Shaping Our View
Sin and Shame 6

God's Intent

Man was free. He lived at peace with God and his wife. He walked and talked with God in an innocent abandon that will never be known on earth again. God saw man, the man that He had created and designed specifically to love, and He said, "It is very good!" God delighted in His creation and called Adam to come and walk with Him and share life with Him. Adam and Eve had complete oneness and unity with each other and their Creator. They were "naked and unashamed."

> "25 Adam and his wife were both naked, and they felt no shame."
> — GENESIS 2:25 NIV

We need to take a very close look at what naked and unashamed mean in order to see what God intended for man. By doing so, we will get a glimpse into the hope we have and the life He intends for us to have even now.

To Live Naked

As we look at the picture that the Genesis account portrays of what life was like before sin entered the heart of mankind, we know that man lived with his wife and his Creator completely naked. The Bible makes this statement in such a way that it seems as if the writer wants us to see something very significant. To live naked seems to mean that they were living without fear.

Adam and Eve did not even know they were naked. They were not ashamed or embarrassed. They had no reason to be. There was nothing to hide in their souls and it was completely evident. They lived in the light.

1. Read 1 John 1:5-7. How does the idea of living naked relate?

_____

_____

_____

To Be Unashamed

To live unashamed before God and others has tremendous meaning. We have stated that shame means to see oneself as having diminished value. It means that our inner sense of value has been lost or lessened because we are less than the standard requires. To live unashamed means that we see our value as it was when God created us.

2. Read Isaiah 61:6-7 and record what God will do to our value.

_____

_____

_____

_____

_____

God is not talking about causing us to live in pride or arrogance in our wealth and abundance. These passages are a portion of the prophecy concerning the new covenant of grace that Christ brought. We can know that God desires to give us a double portion of value or honor. He desires for us to be His crown, His prize and treasure again. This is a condition within our souls that will be evident before men. God longs to restore our understanding of our value as He intended it at creation. He longs for us to live in the light with our souls open and exposed before Him. Only as we live exposed and unashamed are we able to love God and others in a way that fulfills the purpose of man's creation.

Review the *Original Nature* graphic and remember that God created man to walk next to Him in the Garden – God desires to restore our position next to Him. God gave man a purpose; he was to subdue the earth and do this as an eternal being in union with his Creator. God purposes to be known in and through us for all eternity, offering us spiritual purpose and meaning. God wants us to live in the purity that we once had. He knew that along with the knowledge of good and evil would come a hunger to know and experience things that would bring destruction and damage to our souls. He knew that when innocence was lost, evil would captivate the heart of man and the purity of God's image in man would be marred, causing the relationship to be destroyed.

The Condition of Man

There are many ways sin has a devastating impact on the soul of the believer in Christ.

One is the residue of shame that can often stain the soul of those who have been granted forgiveness of sin. How can it be that we have received forgiveness of sin and we have been told over and over how much God loves us, but the effects of sin on our soul can still exist? We try to will ourselves to believe we are free and cleansed yet we still hide our past from others. We don't believe He could ever use us or want to be with us. We don't feel adequate or good enough. We receive His mercy for salvation but somehow living in a relationship with Him with our soul exposed to Him and others seems impossible.

Review the *Sin and Shame* graphic and note that yet another layer of distortion is added to our view of our circumstances, others and our God.

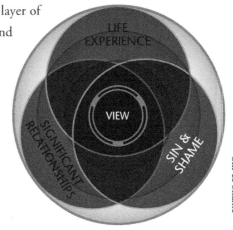

We will look at what God has done to bring about our salvation in a future lesson, but for now we need to understand that the shame that often remains in our souls over our past and sometimes our present sin, shapes and distorts our view of God and others.

1. According to 1 John 4:17-18, where does fear come from? Has that changed?

_____

_____

_____

Shame can do devastating things to our souls. We so often think when we accept Christ as our Savior that there is a big eraser that wipes away the darkness deep within. Yes, we have been forgiven and yes, our debt has been forever erased but sometimes though we experience complete forgiveness from God's point of view, shame is still lurking deep within our souls.

2. Read 1 John 3:19-22 and record what we need to know.

_____

_____

_____

David and Bathsheba

There are numerous stories in God's Word describing sin and its effects on the soul, but none show the consequences of sin to our lives and the lives of others more than the story of David and Bathsheba.

3. Read 2 Samuel 11:1-18; 26-27 and write a brief outline of the story.

_____

_____

_____

_____

_____

_____

_____

_____

_____

David committed both murder and adultery. The consequences that followed in his life were devastating.

4.   Read 2 Samuel 12:7-15 and list the consequences of sin in the life of David.

_____

_____

_____

_____

_____

Shame will rule our souls causing us to hide our souls from the light of God's presence and the acceptance and fellowship He desires for us to experience with others.

As we think about how shame continues to have an affect on the believer in Christ who has experienced forgiveness from sin, lets take a look at how David's shame affected his life and the life of his children.

Amnon and Tamar

The consequences of David's sin reach even further than what we can imagine. We must consider that David had sons who watched him. The reality of the sins of the father being passed down is very evident in David's life as we read more of the story. From his son's perspective David got away with murder and adultery.

5.   Read 2 Samuel 13:1-29 and 14:28-33. Summarize David's response to his son's sin.

_____

_____

_____

_____

_____

Was David's anger alone enough of a response in light of what had been done to Tamar? Why didn't David do something about his sons? Can we blame this on culture alone? While it is true women were not given their rightful place of value in the culture of that time, God had already given the laws protecting women from incest and rape (Deuteronomy 22:28; Deuteronomy 27:22). Could the guilt and shame that damaged David's soul because of his own sin have prevented him from enforcing the laws?

Could it be he did not feel he had the right to expect his children to rise above his own actions? What was in David's mind we cannot know for sure but we can know that the consequences of David's sin were devastating to many.

Sometimes our sense of guilt and shame can cause us to react to others' sin in extreme ways. We may vow our children will not do what we did and become legalistic, harsh, and over protective in how we rear them and deal with their sin. On the other hand, we can be so filled with guilt that we excuse their actions and call it grace and love. Both are reactions to what is inside of us instead of God's desired response based in truth.

Tamar was violated. Her life was destroyed. Because of the sin committed against her, she would no longer be allowed to marry. There was no healing offered to her. Could she have found peace in this? Maybe the customs of the time would not allow her to experience the healing we would like to see or maybe she could not see herself in any other way than used. She tore her clothes and wore ashes of mourning. Her soul was damaged and she "remained desolate in her brother's house." The definition of the word desolate in Hebrew is very descriptive. It means to lose value or to be thrown away as waste.

The Struggle Within

When we commit sin we deem horrible, we will often live feeling we deserve to be punished. Even when we become believers in Christ, we often don't believe we could be forgiven, so we continue to punish ourselves. We develop destructive behaviors ranging from addictions to sabotaging our success in life. We hide away these places in our souls so no one can see or know what is inside. Sometimes we choose not to feel guilt or pain and become harsh and unfeeling towards others. Our personalities are affected as we become critical and judgmental or we become people-pleasers seeking to assuage our guilt through acts of service and kindness.

Sometimes shame can cause us to do strange things. Often we will find ourselves seeking the acceptance from others we cannot find within ourselves. We will tell others of our past sin over and over hoping the understanding and acceptance we get will somehow ease the shame. The attention we get feels like acceptance so we just keep telling our story.

The Sin Around Us

Another way sin affects us has to do with our cultures and the sin that we are exposed to within our families. God gave the Law to His people in the Old Testament with the intent of protecting the purity in the hearts and lives of His people. Yet over and over throughout the history of the Hebrew people they "played the harlot" and went after the gods and immorality seen in the cultures around them. Cultural sin, its lure and hardening effects on their souls blinded them from their own depravity. They followed after the cultural norms of their time and were pulled far away from the God who loved and treasured them. So God promised to put His Spirit within them, to cause them to walk in His ways. Yet we see that for many of us today, resisting the culture around us seems to be a loosing battle.

Driven By Need

Review the *Driven by Need* graphic and the explanation below. Note how fear can drive us to seek to meet our need our way as we allow our culture to shape our view. We are told to "take captive every thought that rises up against the knowledge of God." (II Corinthians 10:5) We flood our minds with scripture promises or praise music to distract our minds that are filled with the things of the world that surround us, yet true purity seems to be reserved for our future eternity as we struggle with thoughts and feelings that are not "held captive" at all. Could it be that we become so calloused to the sin of our culture that we don't see what it does to our souls and the souls of our families.

View through Trust	GOD	View through Fear
We have a need for significance, value and provision		

BELIEF
In my mind I choose what to believe based on how I perceive
my significant relationships, life experience and sin and shame.

God is in control, cares and will determine what my needs are and how they are met	**I am** in control and determine what my needs are and how they are met

PRIORITY
I respond emotionally to what I believe, which determines my priority.

God has my well-being in mind – God and others are important to me	Me–**I can** have whatever I feel will meet my need

DRIVE
With my will, I determine what I will do
to obtain what I believe will satisfy my need based on my priority.

God does what is in my best interest – I will do what pleases God	**I will** pursue what I need to please myself

BEHAVIOR

I choose to wait on God to meet my need as He determines best.	I seek: Power & Position, People & Performance, and Possessions & Pleasure.
Compassion, Kindness, Gentleness, Love	Self-focus, Judgment, Control, Demand

1. Look closely at Ephesians 4:17-24 and record step by step how we are to walk.

_____

_____

_____

_____

_____

_____

2. Read 2 Samuel 13:1-29 again and reflect on the story of Amnon and Tamar.
   Do you think David's sin had an impact on his sons? Record your thoughts.

_____

_____

_____

_____

_____

_____

Remember, the fear that we will not be significant, valued, or have the provision we need is at the core of our being. Sin plays on these fears in deeply impacting ways. When we fear we will not be significant or valued, sin will cause shame to linger deep within, tainting all of our motives. When we fear we will not be valued, we will find ourselves hiding our current sin or our past in an effort to find acceptance and love. In addition, the fear we will not have our needs met can cause us to grow calloused to the sin around us as we embrace what God abhors.

We can rationalize that God doesn't really mean what the Bible says. We tell ourselves; "That was for a different culture and time. That kind of life is an ideal that God does not really expect. Besides if He did, He wouldn't have made us with these needs." The rationalization goes on. The fear that our need will not be met the way we want and in our time frame can even cause us to find Scripture to justify our actions. We will twist His Word to mean what fits our need and ignore God's intent as we rationalize away our sin.

Sin has a devastating affect on our lives through the impurity of our cultures and sin that is seen in our family lives. If we live in a culture where it is acceptable to have many wives, even after becoming a believer in Christ, we can find it very easy to have other women in our lives. If divorce is common in our cultures, we can grow weary of our struggles in marriage and seek the arms of someone who sees us and listens.

If it is normal in our culture to laugh at sin and glorify it in the media, we become calloused to its impact in our lives. It seems that each generation cares less and less about morality of any kind and it is not long before we decide that the Bible is archaic and the purity it calls us to is just not realistic or relevant any more. Even in the church we begin to call sin good and we deem those who stand for purity judgmental and legalistic.

In contrast we can see the affects of sin around us in our cultures, so we isolate our families from the world, all the while hiding the light of God's love and forgiveness from a world that needs it so desperately. We can actually become judgmental and legalistic as we use the Word of God as an implement of destruction instead of an invitation to know this wondrous God of grace and love.

3. Read John 17:13-21 and record what you learn about how we are supposed to live in this world and why?

    _____

    _____

    _____

    _____

    _____

A Look Inside

Read through the following examples of how sin impacts us before you begin to answer the questions.

Cultural Sin

If a culture does not value the sanctity and covenant of marriage as God has ordained in His Word, it will impact even those in the church. Different cultures distort the covenant of marriage in different ways. Some do not value purity before marriage or during marriage and some have even redefined marriage altogether. Some cultures condone multiple spouses and others condone marriage between people of the same sex. When marriage is redefined within a culture and the covenant is not valued it will be difficult, even as believers, to value marriage as God does. When our culture does not value marriage we may:

- decide God's standard is no longer relevant for our culture today and because of grace it is not necessary to maintain the purity He describes in His Word.

- choose to find our sexual satisfaction as we desire without regard to the effects on our marriages, families, or our own souls – examples could be affairs or pornography.

- completely miss the richness and beauty God desires for marital intimacy as we make intimacy only about meeting our physical need.

- grow weary of our spouses so we rationalize our actions as we choose divorce or infidelity in an effort to meet our emotional or physical needs.

Familial Sin

If we have a parent who is an alcoholic, shame will often rule our lives. Sometimes there is abuse (emotional and/or physical) associated with drinking, which can cause deep wounding and suffering. Irresponsibility can bring about a loss of family income. The alcoholic parent can often become a deep embarrassment to the family.

We might:

- be afraid our parent will embarrass us so we treat them poorly in public. Or maybe we avoid being with them. We become secretive and guarded, not allowing others to know us or be near us in relationship.

- fear the abuse that we often experience and seek to please at any cost. We can become people pleasers and yet lose our ability to trust others.

- realize our parents are not dependable so we have to find ways to survive. We can become independent and self-sufficient as we decide we will succeed in life no matter what the cost. We then can become condescending to others who have not overcome as we have.

- become so overwhelmed with the heartache the alcoholic has brought into our lives that we loose hope. We can then follow in their steps, drowning our pain in alcohol.

- become jealous of others who we think have normal lives. We become critical and angry finding ways to hurt others through gossip or slander. We don't want others to have the happiness that has been taken from us.

Personal Sin

Personal sin will cause us to hide our souls away from others. The shame that sin can bring either past or present can have devastating effects on our lives. Sometimes even when we have received forgiveness of sin from God or others we will continue to live with the effects of the shame that it brings. Personal sin can cause us to:

- fear close relationships. We can become harsh and critical, often judging others in an effort to feel better about our own secret sin.

- become lenient and full of understanding making excuses for other's sin so we don't have to think about our own.

- use our past sin as a way to bring attention to ourselves. We can believe that the attention we receive from others is acceptance and value so we keep bringing the focus back to ourselves again and again.

- decide God could never use us so we refuse to function in the gifts and talents that He has given us.

- become calloused to sin as we work hard to eradicate the sense of guilt and shame. We can laugh at the sin around us and take it and its consequences lightly.

As we seek to understand the way sin and shame have shaped our view, keep in mind that our natural tendency is to determine what sin is based on our own understanding. We need to see the devastation of sin from God's perspective. We need to understand it's subtleties and how it destroys relationships. We need to see that our God given need for significance, value and provision has been completely exploited causing us to minimize the impact of sin in our lives so that we continue to meet our needs in our own way. This is the definition of sin. If we don't recognize the problem, we will not seek God's help. He has provided a remedy that we must apply in His way as He enables us. It is so important to do this in a dialogue with your loving Heavenly Father. Please allow adequate time for this portion of the lesson, even if it means spending a few extra days.

1. How did sin affect your ability to see your need for God and His salvation?

_____

_____

_____

_____

_____

_____

_____

2. How has cultural sin affected your attitude and view of sin? Be specific.

_____

_____

_____

_____

_____

_____

_____

3. How has familial sin and shame affected your view of sin? Be specific.

_____

_____

_____

_____

4. How has familial sin affected your sense of personal value? Be specific.

5. What are the ways you hide the shame of your personal sin? What do you do to cover your sin?

6. How has your personal sin affected your view of yourself? Be specific.

7. How have you responded, as a believer, to the sin you see in the world around you? Do you laugh at it, embrace it, excuse it or hide from it?

_____

_____

_____

8.   Do you believe that God is pleased with your attitude towards sin? Why?

_____

_____

_____

_____

_____

_____

_____

As you reflect on the destructive nature of sin it can be overwhelming. Take some time to marvel at the wondrous plan of God. He came into this dark world to rescue us. He has experienced, first hand, the devastation sin has caused. And He paid the price for our freedom. He desires that we live in the freedom that He purchased with His blood. He is an amazing God who loves us more than we can imagine.

In this section "The Drives Within," we will seek to understand our secret motivations and look at the many ways we still operate in the flesh. Please keep in mind that God loves His children intensely. He desires that we reflect who He is to the world. He is faithful and will continue to work on us and accomplish His work in us by His Spirit. We must recognize and agree with Him and allow Him to be our strength.

The Drives Within
Pride and Self-Sufficiency   7

God's Intent

Man was innocent when God created him in the Garden. He lived in a selfless relationship with Almighty God, enjoying all that God had created and all God's presence brought into his life. He did not need to be important or fight for a position before God or Eve. He was content in who he was. Subduing the earth wasn't about dominating through destruction; it was about placing it in order and bringing it under control. Man was created to see himself as the created and God as the all-sufficient creator. Man was both a spiritual and physical being. He was placed in the Garden to fulfill the purpose of his creation, to tend the Garden and subdue the earth as He lived in relationship with His God.

> Then the angel showed me the river of the water of life, as clear as crystal, flowing from the throne of God and of the Lamb ² down the middle of the great street of the city. On each side of the river stood the tree of life, bearing twelve crops of fruit, yielding its fruit every month. And the leaves of the tree are for the healing of the nations. ³ No longer will there be any curse.
>
> — Revelation 22:1-3 NIV

Man's view of himself in the Garden was much different than it is today. Man understood what he had been given and his position and role within creation.

1. Read Revelation 22:1-6 and note the return to the paradise Adam once knew and answer the following questions.

   a. How does God refer to us – what does He call us? (vs. 3-4, 6)

   _____

   _____

   b. What will our role be? (vs. 5)

   _____

   _____

2. Read Exodus 21:1-6 and record what the bond-servant's relationship with the master was like.

   _____

   _____

In the Garden, man's relationship to the earth was to rule over it, yet his relationship with God was one of subjection. He was to rule and yet be ruled over. This is the way it will be in eternity. It is what God desires now. We are to be bond-servants of God seeking His face, living in the light of His presence and yet reigning with Him.

The Condition of Man

But man took his freedom in the Garden, where he lived with little restriction, for granted. He was to obey one simple rule, proving his willing submission to his God. Into the soul of man, something was born that would drive his flesh and prevent him from experiencing the presence of his loving Creator. This drive is pride or self-sufficiency and superiority. Yet, we often like to think of this characteristic as self-confidence or personal competence. So how could this be wrong?

1. Read the following depictions of the angel Lucifer and summarize what happened.

    a. Ezekiel 28:12-17

    _____

    _____

    _____

    b. Isaiah 14:11-15

    _____

    _____

    _____

Lucifer fell from his God ordained position when he wanted to be like God. He fell when he wanted the glory of God. He fell when he no longer wanted to be in submission to God. Pride filled him and he was cast down from the presence of God his Creator.

2. Read Genesis 3:1-5 and note what the serpent specifically said would happen when they ate the fruit of the knowledge of good and evil.

    _____

    _____

    _____

3. Read Genesis 3:22-24 and note what happened to the man and his wife.

    _____

    _____

    _____

As the story of Adam and Eve unfolds before us, we can see that Adam and Eve had a place of spiritual significance and purpose. Their lives had meaning. They lived in relationship with God and they were alive within their spirits to the presence of their creator God. God had created them for a reason. He wanted a relationship with them and he wanted them to rule the earth.

When the serpent tempted Eve, he began by questioning what God had told them. Then he told her that God was withholding something, stating if she ate of the fruit she would be like God. This was the very thing that got the magnificent cherub (guardian angel) cast to earth as a serpent and changed his position in God's spiritual kingdom and order forever.

So man chose to be like God and his place in God's order was changed. Man was sent from the very presence of Living God to live out his existence without the spiritual relationship he was created for. Now his spiritual significance and meaning would always be in question until he came back under the rule of his Creator. Even then, he would not see its complete fulfillment until entering into God's eternal kingdom of heaven.

Pride, the need to regain this place of meaning and position, would now consume all of mankind as he lives in independence and self-sufficiency not trusting the One who created him. Now man would seek to dominate and conquer instead of subdue and he would worship things far from the God that created him. He would forever raise himself above others and essentially place himself in the position of God. Man would demand the right to determine what was good and evil for himself without regard to God's nature, His purposes or His priorities. He would live for himself.

4. Look up the word pride in your dictionary and record a summary of its meaning below.

_____

_____

_____

Man is constantly trying to regain his former state of position, purpose and meaning in his own independent way.

In the Bible, the word for pride in the Greek means to be puffed up. It means to make one seem bigger than they are for the purpose of intimidating others or bringing attention to themselves. Both are based in fear and are designed to keep us in control and bring glory to ourselves.

The Struggle Within

Remember, as we look at pride we must look back at how God created us with spiritual significance through an intimate relationship with Him. Because we fear our lives won't have meaning we try to find that place of purpose by directing and controlling our lives. When we seek to find own place of position through power apart from God, we are living in pride. When we seek to control our own destiny with no thought of God's purposes, we are living in pride.

Speaking of pride as sin is nothing new to us, but most of us struggle to see self-sufficiency and independence as pride, yet these are the very expressions of pride in our lives. The fear that our lives will have no purpose or meaning combines with our life experiences, significant relationships, and our sin to produce expressions of pride that move us far away from the place God intended for us.

Pride in our own abilities is a subtle thing and most people don't regard it as important enough to deal with. In fact, most just label it as self-confidence and move on. But consider that many who walk in pride and self-sufficiency do not know what it means to surrender their souls to Living God. Without this surrender we cannot return to the place in God's purposes we were created for.

What does this mean in itself? If a person has spent their life living and trusting in their own strength and abilities, they are all they count on because they believe they can't count on anything or anyone else. They live in complete independence from God and others. This is by definition rebellion, which is sin.

The sad reality is that most of those who live in pride have very little actual awareness of their inner world at all. The person who is not aware he is dehydrated will never take a drink. The self-sufficient person will think thirst is normal. It is just part of life to be tolerated.

1. Read Galatians 6:3-8 and explain how we are to view ourselves.

   _____

   _____

   _____

2. Read Isaiah 42:8 and record the verse below.

   _____

   _____

   _____

Our pride robs God of His glory and He will not share His glory with another. Glory is the revealed value and worth of something. When we raise ourselves up and seek to be in control of our lives or gain the attention of others, we have demeaned God or robbed Him of the value and worth belonging only to Him.

Many have substituted what they can do for who they are. Very likely because they only felt valued when they were successful in what they did. Nobody cared about who they were. Nobody protected them. Nobody listened to them. Nobody saw them. They learned if they performed well, did things right and did them the best, somebody would pay attention and a small sense of value and significance would seem to be restored.

3. Look at what God says about pride and self-reliance. Summarize the passages below.

    a. I Timothy 6:17-19

    _____

    _____

    b. I Peter 5:5-7

    _____

    _____

    c. I John 2:16

    _____

    _____

The need for significance will cause us to embrace the ways of the world as we seek to gain and keep control of how we establish our position before others and in our own eyes. The need for value and provision will cause us to seek the things of this world, as we will do whatever it takes to take care of ourselves and look good in the eyes of others.

4. Read James 4:1-10 and outline passage.

    _____

    _____

    _____

    _____

    _____

    _____

In the Old Testament God told Moses to tell the people of Israel that He was the great "I AM." (Genesis 3:14) By definition this means that God is all-sufficient and self-sufficient in Himself. This also carries in its meaning that God is the source of everything and all things exist for Him. When man sinned and decided to be like God grasping the right to both experience and determine what is good and evil, he sought to replace the great I Am with himself. Now, from the view within our sinful nature we are the "I am" of our lives. And all things are controlled by us and for us. From our prideful perspective, we have become the center of all things.

Example of the Expressions of Pride

Throughout your childhood you had to learn to survive in your family, both emotionally and physically. You experienced both physical and emotional abuse. As you had to survive your situation, you saw that you could not trust those around you to care for you or protect you. You began to believe that no one could care for you the way you needed, so you would have to care for and protect yourself. Surviving became all that mattered. You determined you would not be hurt or insignificant again so you rose above others. You believed if you could get the upper hand no one would put you down or abuse you again. You became the one in control of your own destiny and now no one can tell you what to do.

Somewhere along the way you came to faith in Jesus Christ. You have surrendered your life to Him as much as you could understand but somehow there are things that still remain in you. You are still independent and self-sufficient and do not need others. You are still brash, opinionated and verbally combative, as you make sure no one has an opportunity to make you feel small again. You can depend on no one to take care of you so you make sure you are in control of your situation. Relationships are still on your terms because you have little to no trust in others. You may even seek to keep others at such a distance that when they get too close to you, you emotionally hurt them before they have the chance to hurt you. All of this is still within your soul even after you came to faith in Christ. Pride still has its roots deep within.

Read Matthew 5:3-5 from the New Living Translation:

> "God blesses those who are poor and realize their need for him, for the Kingdom of Heaven is theirs. God blesses those who mourn, for they will be comforted. God blesses those who are humble, for they will inherit the whole earth."

In the Sermon on the Mount, Jesus said, "God blesses those who are poor and realize their need for Him, for the Kingdom of Heaven is given to them." The word "need" here could be translated in modern terms to be "completely lacking resources of the soul."

He also says, "Blessed are those who mourn for they will be comforted." The Greek word that is translated "mourn" is a term having to do with contrition over sin. Jesus is saying the person who understands the condition and need of their soul and grieves over it will experience the power of His kingdom on earth and the comfort of His presence. This is by definition the very spiritual significance that was lost in the Garden.

A Look Inside

The need for significance and value is at the core of pride. The need to be seen and to matter causes us to place our worth and value above the value of others. It causes us to be self-reliant, critical, and judgmental. Pride robs us of the fellowship of the spirit we should experience with fellow believers. Pride causes us to condemn others who are not as capable in our eyes. We damage our children and spouses as we criticize and pressure them to live up to our standards. We rob others of the opportunity to serve because it is just easier to do it ourselves. At least we will know it is done right.

How can we identify pride within us? Spend a few moments thinking about what it would feel like if others saw you fail. What do you do when you just can't perform at your best? How often do you find yourself criticizing others either in your thoughts or words?

Pride has many expressions in our lives and comes from the fear that is at the core of our soul. Remember, pride is expressed in our lives in the ways we seek attention, honor, and value in the eyes of others. It is seen in how we seek to control our circumstances and the people around us. It is seen in what we do to raise our standing in our own eyes or the eyes of other people.

To meet our need for **significance,** we try to find it through the world's understanding of **power** and **position**.

Review the *Pride and Self-sufficiency* graphic and remember the following:

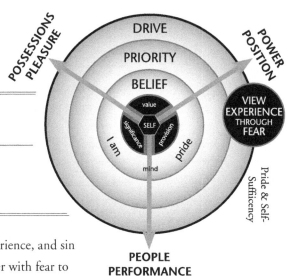

VIEW	The need for significance, value and provision is viewed through fear
BELIEF	**Pride** "**I am**" in control and determine what my needs are and how they are met

Prayerfully reflect again on the significant relationship, life experience, and sin that have impacted your life and how they have worked together with fear to shape your view of life, others, God and yourself.

1. In order to identify expressions of the flesh in our life, we need to reflect on where we are currently. We do things to get our need for significance met that tend to be directed toward gaining control through power and position.

    a. What are the roles or positions you hold? List below your areas of responsibility? (Are you a mother, CEO, pastor, teacher, do you run an office?)

    _____

    _____

_____
_____
_____
_____
_____

b. What do you feel when you are praised or encouraged? How do you respond? Give a specific example.

_____
_____
_____
_____
_____
_____
_____

c. What happens when you are put down or challenged by those over you or under you? How do you respond? Give a specific example.

_____
_____
_____
_____
_____
_____
_____

d. Do you respond to situations, both positive and negative, in the same way you did before you received the Holy Spirit? Explain.

_____
_____
_____
_____
_____
_____

2. Can you identify how significant relationships, life experiences, and sin and shame have worked together to ingrain a pattern of behavior either negative or positive, that have helped you meet your need for significance?

_____

_____

_____

_____

_____

_____

Review the *Expressions of Pride* graphic and note how pride manifests itself through our survival mechanisms (the flesh). When we view our need through fear we seek position and power to fill our need for significance. The evidence of our pride is seen in various expressions in our lives.

3. Circle, or list below, the behaviors that you utilize to gain or retain your position and power to meet your need for significance.

_____

_____

_____

_____

_____

_____

_____

_____

POSSESSIONS PLEASURE

POWER POSITION

opinionated
independent
selfish
self-reliant
deceitful
controlling
critical
value
demanding
self-sufficient
VIEW EXPERIENCE THROUGH FEAR
dominate
arrogant
significance
provision
boastful
seek attention
judgmental

PEOPLE PERFORMANCE

Expressions of Pride

4. We have established that these expressions or behaviors come from fear that our needs will not be met. How do you view these areas of pride? How do you think God views them?

_____

_____

_____

_____

_____

_____

_____

_____

_____

5.   Describe how these areas of pride affect others?

_____

_____

_____

_____

_____

_____

_____

6.   How does this affect your relationship with God?

_____

_____

_____

_____

_____

_____

_____

_____

_____

_____

Pride has indeed invaded the minds of all humans. No one is without pride. Take some time to pray and allow God to show you what He desires for you. Talk to Him about these areas. Remember God is more concerned about why we do what we do than with what we do. Are you motivated by a loving trusting dependence on God, or on self-preservation and self-reliance. Talk to Him about your weakness and inability to trust Him and let Him show you the way.

The Drives Within
Entitlement

8

God's Intent

Contentment filled man's soul before sin entered the world. He lived in wonder and was at peace with his wife and environment (Genesis 2:23). He had his needs met through all that God had made and through the very presence of God.

Man was not aware of any desire for more. He lived in the wonder and delight of paradise. Man did not have expectations or demands. He did not think in terms of what belonged to him or what he should have. There was no clamoring for more of anything. No pursuit of significance or value or possessions. He didn't even know the right of ownership. He had no thought of demanding his personal rights. That didn't happen until the serpent entered the scene.

> ³ And I heard a loud voice from the throne saying, "Look! God's dwelling place is now among the people, and he will dwell with them. They will be his people, and God himself will be with them and be their God. ⁴ 'He will wipe every tear from their eyes. There will be no more death' or mourning or crying or pain, for the old order of things has passed away."
>
> — Revelation 21:3-4 NIV

1. Read Revelation 21:1-7 and 22:1-5. Describe what life will be like when there is no more sin nature at the core of the people of God.

_____

_____

_____

Man's view of heaven is very different than God's. Man typically has himself at the center of a heaven where there is no suffering or pain – where his every desire is met. Man's view of heaven includes getting to be with those who have gone on before him. Man's view of heaven doesn't really include God. His view of heaven may have God making sure all things are good, but certainly doesn't have God as the source and focus of all that is and all that happens. However, the heaven God describes is all about Him and His glory. It is about living in the light of His glory forever and ever. The focus is completely about God, not man. Can you imagine what the world would be like if man were not focused on himself and his need?

It would be like heaven.

The Condition of Man

Unfortunately the reality is that man is completely focused on his own needs and desires. Even those who live very altruistic lives can have self-need wrapped around them that they cannot seem to be free from. This fear driven focus on our needs produces a drive within us called entitlement.

As Eve was informed that she could be like God, pride began to seep into her soul and entitlement took over Eve's life causing her soul's identity to be changed forever. When she handed her husband the fruit, something flooded their souls and self-awareness took over. Satan began to influence Eve's thoughts about herself. She should know the difference between good and evil. She should be like God (pride) gaining her own position in this world. The serpent appealed to her emotion, further enticing her to eat. After all it delighted her eyes so she had a right to it (entitlement). The doubts crept in and her need for personal value was born. The significance and value God had given her was on the verge of being snatched away. She ate, Adam ate, and self-oriented need and desire filled them with fear. From the fear that their core needs would not be met came entitlement. Man now believes he has the right to have his needs met. He has the right to make sure those needs and desires are met no matter what the cost.

1. Look up the word "entitlement" in a dictionary and thesaurus. Summarize what you learn below.

_____

_____

_____

Expectations and Demands

The different expressions of entitlement in our lives can be seen through our expectations and demands.

The 5,000

In the Gospel of John chapter 6, we find the story where Christ fed the 5,000 with a few loaves and fish. Afterward, He went across the Sea of Galilee to escape the crowd that was pressing in on Him. When He got to the other side, He found that the people had followed Him because they realized they would never have to go hungry again if He were in charge, so they decided to make Him king.

2. Read John 6:26-27 and answer the questions that follow.

   a. What were they (the crowd) supposed to be seeking?

   _____

   _____

b. What was Jesus' response? Explain your answer.

_____

_____

_____

_____

_____

The crowd's desire was not to know Jesus or glorify Him. Their desire was to get their physical needs met by Him. They cared nothing of His plans or purposes. They only wanted Him for what they could get from Him. In other passages, because of their demands, He called them an evil and perverse generation.

The Story of Job

Job lost his entire family and possessions – everything except his bitter wife and condescending friends. He was fine for a while – he kept saying he had not sinned, but he did not realize how deep the roots of entitlement had penetrated his soul. He had done everything right. He was moral and upright. He worshipped God and sacrificed on behalf of himself and his family. Yet, God allowed Satan to take his family, his wealth, and his health from him. His friends kept insisting he had done something to deserve what God had allowed and he should just confess so that God would forgive him and relieve his suffering. Job kept insisting he had committed no sin.

3. Read the following passages and summarize Job's attitude toward his situation and God.

a. Job 30:16-23

_____

_____

_____

_____

b. Job 31:5-8

_____

_____

_____

c. Job 31:35-37

_____

_____

_____

For a while Job was willing to suffer without complaint, but eventually there was a problem. He trusted God to make things better for him, to relieve his pain and sorrow, and when he did not hear from God, he began to demand from God an explanation for what God had allowed in his life. This is entitlement.

4. Read and summarize God's response to Job in the following passages.

a. Job 38:1-18

_____

_____

_____

_____

_____

b. Job 40:1-2

_____

_____

_____

_____

_____

How do we know if entitlement is rooted within our souls? We must take a look at how we respond when life and people do not live up to our expectations. The fact we have expectations at all demonstrates that we are prone to this destructive drive. We often think when we have done everything right our teenager just couldn't be pregnant, a drug addict, or an alcoholic. We wonder how our marriage could end the way it did. We served God and went to church. We did and said all of the right things, and yet our loved one is gone. We don't understand why.

Many reading this will experience feelings of anger rise up inside of them as they think of their own unfulfilled expectations. Eve believed she had a right to all of the fruit in the Garden. She believed she had a right to have her appetites satisfied. She thought she had a right to understanding and knowledge, which God had not chosen to give her. She had a right to whatever her eyes thought desirable. Entitlement was born in the Garden. Job trusted God to be to him what he expected, but eventually when God was silent and did not give a justifiable reason for what He had allowed in Job's life, he began to demand an explanation from God. Whenever our desires reach the level of demand we know we are responding to life in entitlement.

Entitlement is a drive that comes out of the fear that our needs will not be met. It is the motivation behind our will that determines our actions.

Study carefully the *Entitlement* graphic.

VIEW	The need for significance, value and provision is viewed through fear
BELIEF	**Pride** "**I am**" in control and determine what my needs are and how they are met
PRIORITY	**Entitlement** Me—"**I can**" have whatever I feel will meet my need

Note, at the core is the fear that our need for significance, value, and physical provision will not be met. This in turn combines with our significant relationships, life experiences, and the impact of sin in our lives to form our view and perceptions (mind) as we process our lives and relationships. This forms our beliefs, which determines what is important to us (emotions), or our priorities. From out of our priorities comes the drives (will) that determine our actions and behaviors.

The Struggle Within

In many cultures, people see themselves as victims. We live in a world that tells us repeatedly that we need empowerment and we have a right to be heard. The TV tells us how much we need material things. We're told we all have personal rights, and we're taught to believe our personal rights are somehow more important than those of anyone else. We have turned self-confidence into personal promotion and life goals into personal agenda. We have become self-oriented societies promoting personal need and desire above all else.

When we look into our own lives, as believers in Christ, we find the roots of entitlement so deeply embedded in the fabric of our soul that it can drain us of any loving movement towards God and others. We treat God more like a Santa Claus or a genie. We demand that He make our lives happy and our church experience fulfilling. We expect if we do our duty then He will surely come through for us in the way we desire. Somehow it appears as if He owes us.

In the mind-set of entitlement, the concept of "take up your cross and follow me" only applies to pastors and missionaries. Convenience has taken the place of commitment and common experience has replaced the loving community God desires.

Most of us would say we are not this bad. We have what we consider loving relationships. However, we begin to see how deeply the roots of entitlement reach into our souls when we evaluate the way we respond to God and others as our expectations are not met. When our spouses don't love us the way we think we need to be loved or if they don't love us well at all, we can hear ourselves saying "If they would only…" When our children don't live up to our expectations, we make demands that they ignore and we ask "what did I do to deserve this heartache?" When our friends disappoint us or hurt us, we put up boundaries and say it is for the best; sometimes we even say it is for their good.

Sometimes even our relationships with God can take entitlement to an even greater level. Too often, even our movement toward God is more to satisfy our soul with a spiritual experience than it is a genuine desire to be with Him, glorify Him and love Him with abandon. We come to God because we need something from Him not because He is God and is more than deserving of our time, attention, and adoration.

1. Read the passages below and list what God has to say about the rights of those who love and serve Him. Be specific.

    a. Philippians 2:5-8

    _____

    _____

    _____

    _____

    _____

    _____

    b. Philippians 3:1-8

    _____

    _____

    _____

    _____

    _____

A Look Inside

How we feel and respond inside during the difficult times of life will tell us how deeply the roots of entitlement have wound down into the core of our soul. When we feel God owes us an explanation, entitlement exists within us. When our constant question is "Why has God done this to me?" or "Why has He allowed this to happen?" entitlement is there. When we demand that others treat us fairly or justly, entitlement reigns in our souls.

1. In order to identify entitlement in our own lives, we need to consider the things we believe we have a right to.

   a. What are the rights, possessions or positions you hold on to?

   _____

   _____

   _____

   _____

   _____

   _____

   _____

   b. What do you feel when your possessions or pleasures are threatened? How do you respond? Give specific examples.

   _____

   _____

   _____

   _____

   _____

   _____

   _____

   _____

   _____

   _____

   _____

   c. What do you feel when your position before others or your control over situations is threatened? How do you respond? Give specific examples.

   _____

   _____

   _____

   _____

   _____

   _____

   _____

   _____

   _____

d. What do you feel when you are devalued in the eyes of others or when you do not have the approval or love of others? How do you respond?
Give specific examples.

_____

_____

_____

_____

_____

_____

_____

_____

_____

_____

_____

_____

_____

_____

_____

_____

_____

_____

2. Review the *Expressions of Entitlement* graphic and list below the indications of entitlement in your own life.

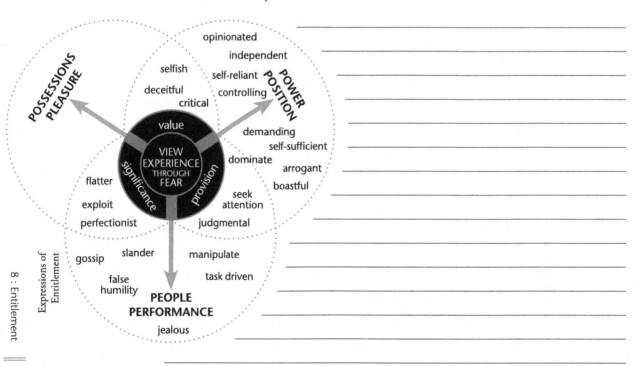

POSSESSIONS
PLEASURE

POWER
POSITION

selfish
deceitful
critical

opinionated
independent
self-reliant
controlling

value

demanding
self-sufficient
dominate
arrogant
boastful

VIEW
EXPERIENCE
THROUGH
FEAR

significance

provision

flatter
exploit
perfectionist

seek
attention
judgmental

gossip   slander   manipulate
false   task driven
humility

**PEOPLE
PERFORMANCE**

jealous

3.   Summarize how entitlement has affected you.

_____

_____

_____

_____

_____

_____

_____

_____

_____

_____

_____

_____

_____

_____

_____

4.   Summarize how the entitlement in you has affected those you love.

_____

_____

_____

_____

_____

_____

_____

_____

_____

_____

_____

_____

_____

_____

_____

_____

5.   How has entitlement affected your view of God and your relationship with Him?

_____

_____

_____

_____

_____
_____
_____
_____
_____
_____
_____
_____
_____
_____
_____
_____
_____
_____
_____
_____
_____
_____

The contrast between how you live and what God desires can cause you to feel
frustrated. Some will vacillate between anger and grief, recognizing the entitlement
that reigns over their souls. You can neither remove entitlement from your soul nor will
yourself to behave differently, however you can invite the Living God to do His work
and then let Him do it.

The Drives Within
The Pursuit of Pleasure 9

God's Intent

God intended for man to share in His joy over His creation. After God created everything, He looked at all He had done and said it was good. He made man in His image to enjoy what He enjoyed. He made man to delight in beauty and to enjoy the experience of spiritual significance of purpose as he fulfilled his roll as a part of creation.

> "The worth and excellency of a soul is to be measured by the object of its love."
> — HENRY SCOUGAL

1. Read Genesis 1:26-30 and Genesis 2:15,18-20 and record man's relationship to the things of the earth.

_____

_____

_____

_____

_____

_____

_____

Man was created in the image of God to love beautiful things. Man was created to experience pleasure and delight through his senses. He was created to enjoy taste, touch, smell, and the wonder of hearing. He was created to take in the beauty of his surroundings and experience it with profound pleasure. And as he did, man would see the glory of his God.

2. Read the following passages and record what God desires to reveal through our senses.

a. Psalm 8

_____

_____

b. Psalm 19:1-3

_____

_____

_____

Man was created with the ability to experience pleasure. God invited man to take pleasure in His creation when He told him to subdue the earth and tend the Garden. In man's initial innocent state this would have been a truly wondrous experience. Through these experiences, man is able to see a glimpse of his God.

The Condition of Man

Pride and entitlement entered into mankind in the Garden and man's soul was changed forever. Instead of their souls living in purity, serving in humility and delighting in gratitude for all that God had given them, Adam and Eve and all of their children (us) would forever be driven by the perceived need for more. Self-oriented entitlement joins with our perceived needs and natural appetites to create a pursuit of pleasure within us, as we seek to obtain what we believe will satisfy our needs any way we can. This is called idolatry.

It seems like idolatry is one of those words that applied in biblical times when people bowed in barbaric worship to things fashioned from wood and stone, made by the hand of man. The reality is, we still worship things fashioned by the hand of man as we bow to the gods of pleasure and possessions.

In order to understand idolatry, we must understand the full meaning of worship. Finding our soul's home and place of deepest satisfaction requires that we come before Living God with our souls in complete abandon to Him in worship. When we look at the New Testament concept of worship, we know it means to bow before something or someone in subjection and adoration. It means to give allegiance. If we look at the visual of bowing before something or someone it means we are at its mercy. In other words, it has the upper hand and is in control. A very good definition of worship is "Your response to what has captured your soul."

How do we find ourselves at the mercy of other things instead of living in the love and mercy of our gracious Heavenly Father? The word for idolatry in the Greek comes from a root word meaning "to see with your eyes." If we look back to the Garden of Eden we can see that idolatry was birthed as Eve saw the fruit "was a delight to the eyes" (Genesis 3:6). When Adam and Eve ate the fruit, the hunger to have more was born into all mankind. The result is man is never satisfied. He never seems to have enough.

Possessions

In the New Testament, idolatry was often associated with greed and covetousness. In other words, from a New Testament perspective it began to have less to do with images carved from stone or wood. Idolatry began to mean the pursuit of what pleases us. Pleasure is made up primarily of the enjoyment of possessions and the way people make us feel.

These are things that can captivate our hearts and minds in ways so subtle we would not even recognize we are bowing to them, nor would we ever dream we are at their mercy. However, if we consider what our lives would be like if one or more of these things were to be removed, we will quickly see how much we are living in subjection to them.

Many of us may think possessions will bring a sense of security to our lives, but it seems the more things we have, the more time we spend worrying about losing them. If our eyes are constantly looking towards possessions (the root of idolatry) we will find our focus far from Living God. The manifest presence of Living God does not exist in wood or stone made for the pleasure of our flesh or the protection of our personal value or security. He exists in the sanctuary of our soul.

1. Read Mark 10:17-31 and answer the questions.

    a. Why do you think Jesus required what He did?

    _____
    _____
    _____
    _____
    _____

    b. What is the principle Jesus is trying to get across?

    _____
    _____
    _____
    _____
    _____

When we hold on to whatever we have, in fear of losing it or not having enough, we are living in idolatry and greed. This can be very subtle. It is not about quantity; it is about dependency. We are bowing at the foot of the idol of possessions. We can work hard to feed our families every day and still find ourselves filled with idolatry as we see what others have and long for what is not ours. We can horde our money and possessions, giving just enough to the work of God to assuage our guilt, but never giving freely. We can fret and worry constantly that we will not have enough.

2. Read Luke 14:31-33 in the New International Version below.

    31 "Or suppose a king is about to go to war against another king. Won't he first sit down and consider whether he is able with ten thousand men to oppose the one coming against him with twenty thousand? 32 If he is not able, he will send a delegation while the other is still a long way off and will

ask for terms of peace. [33] In the same way, those of you who do not give up everything you have cannot be my disciples."

The words "give up" in the Greek actually mean "to place in their proper order."

This verse means all we have should be put into its proper perspective and priority in our lives according to God's purposes and priorities.

People

Another form of idolatry is the place people hold in our lives. Many of us place a huge value on relationships and interaction. Often this can be primarily for the sake of feeling loved and being valued. Again, feeling loved and being valued are not wrong, but when being loved by others and seeking their approval captivates our hearts and drives our motives, what seems to be good intentions can become self-seeking bondage. We can find our giving designed to bring us acceptance and the return of another's affection. The tangible, visible affirmation of others captivates our hearts. We allow the need to be loved by others to cause us to bow to them. Our need for belonging and acceptance causes us to be controlled by those we love. We bow to the need for love again and again as we compromise and manipulate in order to gain approval.

So how do we know when our relationships have become too much about us? We must always look at why we do what we do. We must look beneath the surface of our actions that seem loving and giving in our relationships to see if our desire is truly for the benefit of others and not just for approval and belonging. We will know what our motives are when others do not live up to our expectations in relationships. We will understand how deeply we seek to meet our own need when we see how we respond to those who do not love us as we believe they should or when people fail to give us the recognition and position in their lives we feel we deserve. Our need to be loved by our families, our spouses, and our friends can all captivate our hearts more than the love of our Lord and Savior if we are not careful.

3. Read Matthew 10:37-39. What are our priorities in relationships supposed to be?

_____

_____

_____

Jesus says we are to love Him above all other relationships (Luke 14:26), but how do we know when we are not giving Him the highest place in our souls? We must examine our thought life. How much time and emotional energy do we spend reviewing our conversations with others as we search for signs of disapproval? How much time do we spend trying to figure out ways we can improve our standing in the eyes of others instead of Him. These motives are incredibly subtle, but they rob us of the ability to love God genuinely and receive love from Him without fear, for we tend to relate to Him in much the same way as we do others.

4. Read through Genesis 22:1-19 and list its main points. What was God trying to show Abraham in this story?

_____

_____

_____

_____

_____

_____

_____

_____

_____

The Struggle Within

God desires your whole heart. He will not share this place of worship with another. He tells us we are to have no other gods before Him. This means we can give nothing other than God our full allegiance. We can bow to nothing except Him.

What has captivated your soul? What things or relationships do you hold on to tightly? As long as idolatry has even the slightest foothold in your heart it will hinder your ability to apprehend Living God. You will struggle to keep your gaze focused on God, your provider.

1. Read and summarize Matthew 6:25-33.

_____

_____

_____

_____

_____

The pursuit of pleasure or idolatry is a drive within the soul that comes from fear. The fear within us leads to unbelief and exists at the core of the soul of natural man. Again if we look at what is at the core of our fear we will see that our need to have our physical needs met works together with our life experiences and sinful culture to produce within us idolatry, which, in turn leads to greed.

As we consider the possibility of idolatry being present in our lives, remember idolatry and worldly pursuits can be very subtle. They are often very difficult to recognize.

VIEW	The need for significance, value and provision is viewed through fear
BELIEF	**Pride** "**I am**" in control and determine what my needs are and how they are met
PRIORITY	**Entitlement** Me–"**I can**" have whatever I feel will meet my need
DRIVE	**Idolatry** "**I will**" pursue what I need to please myself
BEHAVIOR	Self-focus, Judgment, Control, Demand I seek: Power & Position, People & Performance, and Possessions & Pleasure

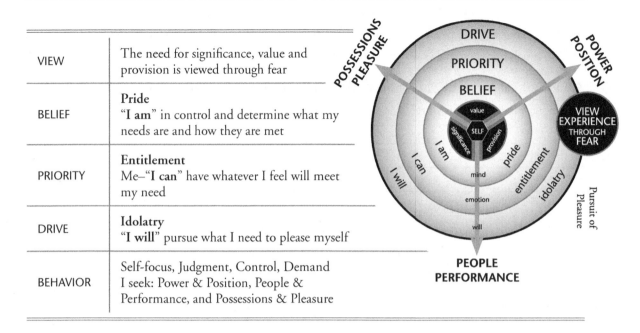

Review the *Pursuit of Pleasure* graphic and consider the internal path to idolatry with the following scenarios.

Scenario 1

Maybe as a child your family lived in poverty (life circumstances). You never had enough food (core physical need) and your parents worked constantly to survive. You went to sleep many nights with hunger gnawing at your insides and your heart aching because of the shame of being ridiculed for your tattered clothes (mind and perceptions). You began to believe that no one would ever meet your need. As you lay awake in the night, a hunger for more took hold of your soul (emotions). You vowed you needed to have what others had (value) so you would rise above this life (will) and idolatry (a fleshly drive) began to wind itself deep within your soul. You determined you would do whatever you needed to in order to enjoy the things that other people had.

Scenario 2

Or maybe, when you were a child, your family had all that they could possibly need and more (life experience). You never lacked anything and if you needed something you went and got it. As you grew up you began to believe that somehow you deserved it (your view - mind). As an adult you would never be satisfied (emotions) with less than you had as a child (belief). You needed to maintain this lifestyle (value) so you determined (will) you would do whatever you needed (fleshly drive - idolatry) to maintain the lifestyle you once knew.

Scenario 3

Or perhaps, as a small child you had a special relationship with your father. He spent time with you and paid attention to you (significant relationship). Then when you were a little older he abandoned the family, and found another family to love (life circumstance). You believed you were partly responsible for his departure (your view - mind). If you had just been a better child maybe he would have stayed (your belief). You began to try to find ways to earn his love and bring him back into your life, but things were never the same. You felt abandoned (emotions). You determined (will) within your soul that you would never allow that kind of hurt to happen again. You began to seek the approval of those you are in relationship with (fleshly drive) through the right behavior or loving actions that are designed to win and keep others in relationship with you. Relationships and the approval of people (idolatry) became a primary motivation as you serve God and others.

If we think about what life would be like if we removed the things we value most in this life, we will be able to see where idolatry is lurking within our souls. It may not be just one thing; it may be an entire lifestyle to which we bow. Consider that these things we bow to don't bring us comfort when we are hurting. They don't fill us with the fullness of their presence. They cannot delight in us. They give very little back to us beyond the immediate gratification of our flesh and the obligation to care for and maintain them.

A Look Inside

When we worship anything other than God, whether it is pleasure, possessions or people, the Bible tells us we are committing spiritual adultery. God calls those who seek after other gods "harlots." Our souls are not able to respond to Him fully and we are not able to experience the spiritual fullness He desires.

You may think this is really strong language and you are not deserving of these words. However most of us bow to something or someone. There are few in this world that do not struggle with being controlled by something other than God, especially during the difficult times of life or relationships.

We run to all kinds of things to satisfy us or make us feel better. These things become our god and we find ourselves at their mercy. Seeking our gracious Heavenly Father is typically a last resort.

1. List the things in your life you value the most. You will know what they are by how much time you spend trying to gain and keep them – remember, people can be listed here.

_____

_____

_____

_____

_____

_____

_____

2. As you consider these things, take a look at the graphic *Expressions of Idolatry* and lists you have made concerning your past circumstances and significant relationships. Based on these lists, can you see where the need to gain or keep something came from? When in your past have you not had enough? What did you lack?

_____

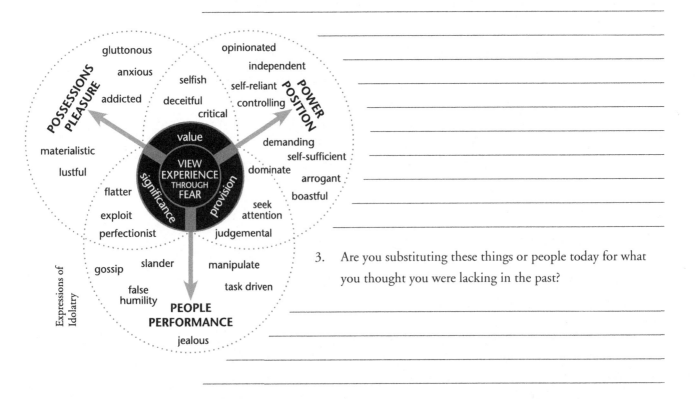

Expressions of Idolatry

_____

_____

_____

_____

_____

_____

_____

3. Are you substituting these things or people today for what you thought you were lacking in the past?

_____

_____

_____

_____

Letting go of what you think will satisfy you, and trusting that what He has for you is all you need, is more than you are capable of doing apart from His Spirit. Trust that He will show you. Most do not believe what He has for us is better than what we are holding to so tightly. Do not be deceived.

God has not hidden the way to Him. He shows us clearly in His Word how to know Him and His ways. He has made a way to restore our relationship with Him. In 2 Samuel 14:14, it says that God devises a way to bring us back when we have been separated from Him. As we look at the unbelief that leads to lack of trust in our souls, we will see the need for repentance. We are not asking you to repent over the sins of your past. We are asking you to look at your unbelief and recognize how the lack of trust is the sin that causes your fleshly behavior. This is what you need to repent from.

The Renewed Mind
Believing God   *10*

God's Intent

God calls man to live in the trusting love relationship he was created for. God desires to walk with us in His eternal kingdom where His Spirit can move freely through our souls. He wants us to know the unity that we once experienced with Him – the unity that exists in the Godhead. He wants us to experience that love and unity even now.

> ⁶ And without faith it is impossible to please God, because anyone who comes to him must believe that he exists and that he rewards those who earnestly seek him.
>
> — HEBREWS 11:6 NIV

God has not left us without a way. God set in motion a plan for restoration that would bring man back to the purity and fellowship of that relationship for all eternity. From the moment man fell from his position and shame entered his soul, driving him from the presence of his creator, God had a plan to restore man's relationship and place of spiritual significance. However, the very belief that faded from the heart of man that fateful day would be the key to the restoration.

God does not change; the basis for the relationship would not change. It would all hinge on restoring man's belief in God. It would require faith. That belief would not be based on what was understood in the mind alone, but what was experienced as an undeniable conviction of the soul. It would not be based on a set of rituals. It would be based in belief that leads to complete trust.

1. Read the following passages and record the importance of belief and what it brings.

    a. John 5:24

    _____

    _____

    b. John 11:25-26

    _____

    _____

    c. John 17:20-24

    _____

    _____

The Condition of Man

Adam and Eve sinned when they no longer believed God had their wellbeing at the center of His heart. They wondered if they were missing something, which moved them toward rebellion and disobedience. They sinned and found themselves hiding behind bushes and fig leaves for protection. They were separated from the presence of their Creator and the lover of their souls. Sin entered the soul of all of mankind. Now all men are born spiritually separated from God, which means they are spiritually dead. Until we come to faith in God through Jesus Christ, there will be a chasm that separates us from the presence of the One who loves us; the One we were created to love.

Study *The Struggle Within* graphic. The fearful unbelieving soul sees life circumstances, significant relationships along with sin and shame through fear, which leads to unbelief. Fear and unbelief exploit our basic needs to be valued and to have our needs met. Fear causes drives within us that find their expression through the flesh that we call survival mechanisms. This is the pattern that was laid down by Adam and is imprinted in our souls. Now as believers in Christ we have been given the power to choose whether we will live in trust or be ruled by fear.

The Struggle Within

DRIVE
PRIORITY
BELIEF

POSSESSIONS PLEASURE
POWER POSITION

VIEW EXPERIENCE THROUGH TRUST
VIEW EXPERIENCE THROUGH FEAR

value
significance — GOD — provision
humility / pride
gratitude / entitlement
devotion / idolatry
mind
emotion
will

PEOPLE PERFORMANCE

VIEW EXPERIENCE THROUGH TRUST	Choosing Trust	GOD	Choosing Fear	VIEW EXPERIENCE THROUGH FEAR

We have a need for significance, value and provision

Humility ← **BELIEF** → Pride

In my mind I choose what to believe based on how I perceive my significant relationships, life experience and sin and shame.

God is in control, cares and will determine what my needs are and how they are met	"**I am**" in control and determine what my needs are and how they are met

Gratitude ← **PRIORITY** → Entitlement

I respond emotionally to what I believe, which reveals my priority.

God has my well-being in mind– God and others are important to me	Me–"**I can**" have whatever I feel will meet my need

Devotion ← **DRIVE** → Idolatry

With my will, I determine what I will do to obtain what I believe will satisfy my need based on my priority.

God does what is in my best interest – I will do what pleases God	"**I will**" pursue what I need to please myself

Bond-servant ← **BEHAVIOR** → Self-focused

I choose to wait on God to meet my need as He determines best. Compassion, Kindness, Gentleness, Love	I seek: Power & Position, People & Performance, and Possessions & Pleasure. Self-focus, Judgment, Control, Demand

Understanding Belief

Unbelief is devastating to our lives. Most of us don't even recognize the unbelief within our souls. We say God is enough to satisfy our souls, yet we constantly seek more in this life – more control, more things, more fun, more love. We sing praise music expressing His power and might, yet we clamor for our position in social ranking, on ministry committees and in relationships. We claim to know He loves us, yet we are constantly driven to find love and acceptance. We say He is righteous in all of His ways, yet we seek to control others and the circumstances in our lives. We say we believe He is fair and good, yet "why me?" or "why them?" rolls off our tongues with ease, while anxiety in its various expressions tears up our insides. How real is our belief?

1. Look up the word "belief" in your dictionary and write its definition below.

_____

_____

In Hebrew the term for belief means "to be firmly established, enduring, or unwavering in conviction." *Vines Expository Dictionary* describes belief in a powerful word picture, "belief is like the place into which a peg will be driven so that it will be immovable. The peg will remain firmly anchored, even though it is pushed so hard that it breaks off at the point of entry."

What you believe

BELIEF

What we truly believe is represented by the peg, and belief is what the peg is driven into. With this in mind, we can know that the things we are holding tightly to are what we truly believe and the evidence of our belief will be seen in our lives.

Belief holds on to what it knows so firmly that what it knows could be broken or destroyed and the soul would still not let it go. Is what you believe about God so firmly planted in your soul it would not be shaken even if God *seemed* to stop being who He is? Can you say you believe so strongly in the love, power, and fairness of God that even if those attributes *seemed* to fail, you would still hold to them as if your very existence depended on it? As you exercise this belief it turns to trust.

Belief is not just mental recognition. It means to be so deeply convinced of something that it governs your actions. When trauma happens and life or people get difficult, what governs your actions? Likewise, what governs your actions when life becomes routine and lifeless?

2. Read the passages below and explain how you think they relate to belief.

   a. Philippians 1:29-30

_____

_____

_____

b. Philippians 2:12-13

_____

_____

_____

c. Mark 9:17-24

_____

_____

_____

d. James 1:6-8

_____

_____

_____

Belief is a choice, but it is also enabled and empowered by God. If you struggle with belief ask God to increase your ability to believe. Exercise the belief you have and move towards God. What God desires is for you to turn the gaze of your soul towards Him. He will work within you and cause circumstances in your life to increase your faith. He can and will give you the belief that leads to the trust you need within your soul so you can hold tightly to the things of God, which will both satisfy you and bring about the soul transformation He desires.

The Struggle Within

We are physical beings living in a temporal world. Yet we are also spiritual beings designed for God's eternal kingdom. This dichotomy causes us to struggle to give God our allegiance and trust. In order for us to trust fully in God's specific attributes we need to understand His priorities. God's ways are not our ways and His thoughts are not our thoughts (Isaiah 55:8-9). Our natural man sees only what is happening in the immediate and physical experiences of life (what is temporal), yet God's perspective reaches into eternity. Because of God's spiritual and eternal perspective, He will always make the spiritual and eternal His priority over the physical and temporal. God will also always be more concerned with our internal condition. He will always be more concerned with our motives and attitudes than with right behavior. There must be a shift in our perspective. We cannot expect and demand that God will make what is important to us in the temporal and physical His priorities.

What are the things we need to understand and believe about God that will help to free us from the survival mechanisms (flesh) that keep us in bondage to our natural man? What are the things we need to know and stake our lives on that will cause us to love

God with abandon and love others without reservation? There are numerous attributes of God we could explore, but for our purposes we will look briefly at the three basic groups of attributes we studied in lesson two.

God's Justice and Righteousness (Holy Attributes)

Justice means to judge fairly and equitably. Righteousness means He always does what is right based on what He has determined is fair. It also means He judges what is fair based on the fact He knows what is right. Remember, God's justice and righteousness is based on His eternal and spiritual perspective and not on the physical and temporal world we see.

1. Read the following passages and list what you find about God's justice and righteousness.

    a. Deuteronomy 32:3-4

    _____

    _____

    _____

    b. Jeremiah 23:3-6

    _____

    _____

    _____

    c. Psalm 119:75-77

    _____

    _____

    _____

Attributes of God

HOLY

God's justice and righteousness.

He is just and right in all He does.

SOVEREIGN

God's position and ability.

He is all powerful, completely

able and in total control.

RELATIONAL

God's love and goodness.

He loves unconditionally.

He always does what is in

our best interest for our good

and His glory.

Too often we evaluate what God is doing and allowing on the basis of our own sense of justice and righteousness. Man's righteousness is based on benefiting his own need and is governed by his personally determined sense of fairness. Man is the center of his or her world, and our concepts of righteousness are founded entirely on what is best for us from our limited and relative understanding of time, events, and morality.

2. Explain below how an unshakable belief in God's justice and righteousness could affect your drive and need to protect your soul. How would your life be different if you really believed and trusted that God always did and allowed what is right and fair based on His spiritual and eternal perspective and priorities? How would it affect your behavior?

    _____

    _____

10 : Believing God

_____

_____

_____

_____

_____

God's Position and Ability (Sovereign Attributes)

Many, whether in the secular or Christian community, struggle to believe that God is all-powerful. We look at the world today and it just doesn't make sense that God would allow what is going on if He could in any way stop it. When we think of starvation and the lives torn apart by war, we cannot understand how a good and all-powerful God would allow these things to happen. If God is all-powerful, shouldn't He do something? When we look at the cataclysmic natural disasters the world has experienced in the past we cannot believe God would allow such devastation and destruction to human life. Wasn't He watching? Didn't He see this coming? Again our view of God's sovereignty is often skewed by our concepts of what is good, fair, and right.

Some believe God created the world then stepped back to let man fight it out on his own. They believe He might step into history occasionally to direct His overall purposes but man is left, for the most part, to deal with life on his own.

3.   Look up the word "sovereignty" in your dictionary and summarize its definition.

_____

_____

_____

Sovereignty is defined from a biblical understanding as "the authority, power, right, and knowledge to rule." It includes all of the natural attributes of God: omnipotence (all powerful), omnipresence (everywhere at once), and omniscience (all knowing). He is also immutable (never changing), eternal, and transcendent (He is beyond anything we could think or imagine). These natural attributes are then governed by His holiness or moral attributes.

In order for God to rule all things, He must have power over all things. In order for Him to have power over them, He must be present at all times and He must know all things that happen and that are going to happen. In order for God to rule and order the universe, He must be consistent in how He chooses to interact with His created world; He is immutable. In order for Him to rule in power, His rule must never end; He is eternal. For God to be able to rule over all things, He must be greater than anything created. He must also be greater than His creation could ever imagine.

For some it may be easy to say God is all-powerful and He rules over all of creation, but until we examine what specifically He rules over and how His rule specifically affects us, we will constantly seek to control people and circumstances. We must trust His sovereign rule.

4. Look at the passages below and fill in the chart:

What God rules over	How God rules	Evidence in life
Daniel 4:28-37		
Lamentations 3:37-38		
Psalm 24:1-2		
Exodus 4:21		
Jeremiah 24:7		
I John 3:19-20		

Can God really be in control of all that happens in the created universe? So many questions rise up in our souls as we contemplate the possibility that God is indeed sovereign. Many struggle to believe God can be sovereign while man retains his free will. One of the greatest mysteries of God is how the sovereignty of God can work together with the free will of mankind to accomplish His purposes, our good, and His glory. Yet Scripture supports these seemingly contradictory principles. This study does not allow room for a thorough theological discussion concerning how these two realities work together; what we desire here is to establish within our souls the truth that God rules completely over all. How it works is a mystery even the most learned theologians struggle to understand and explain.

Being Renewed © 2017 AP – rev 04.18

5. Explain your belief in God's Sovereignty. Do you believe God governs all that happens in your life? Does He just step in from time to time when He can? Is He ever surprised at what has happened? What is evidence of your belief?

_____

_____

_____

_____

_____

God's Love and Goodness (Relational Attributes)

It is easier to see the love of God as it relates to all of mankind through salvation. However, we can often struggle to understand a love so real and so tangible that it can literally fill and transform our soul. We believe God loves us enough to save us from eternity in hell, but would He really want to know us? Would He really love us enough to want to be with us and delight in us?

When we believe we must be worthy of love, we are putting limits on our experience of God's love for us. To us, His love becomes conditional to our sense of personal value.

Most of us know in our minds God is love and we will say He loves us personally. However, we often understand the depths of our experience of His love on the basis of how we view our own worth. The reality is that we do not always believe we are worthy of the incredible love of God, but somehow we confuse our intrinsic worth with the experience of the value God has given to us. God does not love us because we have done something to earn His love or because we are more spiritual or lovable. He does not love us because we can give anything back to Him. He doesn't even love us because He sees all of our potential. He loves us because He created us and wants an intimate relationship with us. He loves us with a standard of value we do not understand. He loves us for the pure joy of loving. He loves us in order to be and express who He is – the God who is love, the God whose nature defines love. He loves us and that love itself gives us value beyond what we could ever imagine. God loves to love us! To be loved by God; what greater value could we have?

6. Look up the word "love" in your dictionary and write out its definition.

_____

_____

The Greek word used to describe God's love for us is unique to the New Testament. It is an unconditional, self-sacrificing love that causes Him to always do what is best and good for us.

10 : Believing God

7. Read the following passages and record how knowing, believing, and experiencing this kind of love should affect the survival mechanisms expressed in your life. Be specific.

    a. I John 4:9-10, 16-19

    _____

    _____

    _____

    _____

    _____

    _____

    b. Romans 8:31-39

    _____

    _____

    _____

    _____

    _____

    _____

Do you know what it means to experience the fullness of Christ's love for you? God's love for you cannot be experienced as a mental exercise. It is not just theology. His love is more than just a reality that won your soul's place in heaven. He desires to fill your soul to the point of overflowing with the intimate experience of real, tangible love.

Our experience of His love will be dramatically limited by the self-protection surrounding our soul. Our carnal or fleshly soul will never be able to fully embrace His love.

A Look Inside

The concept of belief is difficult. We would like to think we have a strong belief, however we may find our belief doesn't reach very deep into our souls. Most of us begin to struggle when disasters happen, when we experience wounding or when we are driven by the guilt and shame of our past. When we are faced with these painful things, we will often believe God is either all-powerful, but not fair and loving, or He is loving and good but not really in control. How could we be faced with these things if He was indeed all-powerful, all loving, and completely right and fair in all of His ways? Some of us believe He is all of those things to others but not to us. We may feel we are somehow not worthy when others are.

1. Based on what you learned about belief in this session, how strong would you rate your belief in the various attributes of God (with a "1" meaning no belief at all, and "10" being complete, immovable trust). Remember your survival mechanisms demonstrate the level of your belief. Circle the appropriate place number and explain your answer in the space provided.

    a. **God's Justice and Righteousness** (Holiness)

    0 – 1 – 2 – 3 – 4 – 5 – 6 – 7 – 8 – 9 – 10

    _____

    _____

    _____

    _____

    _____

    b. **God's Position and Ability** (Sovereignty)

    0 – 1 – 2 – 3 – 4 – 5 – 6 – 7 – 8 – 9 – 10

    _____

    _____

    _____

    _____

    _____

    c. **God's Love and Goodness** (in Relationship)

    0 – 1 – 2 – 3 – 4 – 5 – 6 – 7 – 8 – 9 – 10

    _____

    _____

    _____

    _____

    _____

In the next lesson we will explore exactly what God has done that gives us the ability to trust Him. We will look at the work He has done to restore and secure our spiritual significance. We will see how He has demonstrated the great value He has ascribed to us and how He desires to use the temporal and physical world to transform our souls through the work of His Spirit.

The Renewed Mind
Trusting His Work 11

God's Intent

God desires freedom for our souls. He desires that we live by grace, not bound by rules and regulations. He wants us to live in a relationship that is evidenced by peace and rest. He desires that we love Him with abandon and others without reservation. This is only possible if we experience the soul transformation that He desires. As His image is restored in us we will have the ability to know and experience Him and He will have the ability to move freely in and through us.

> [8] Let the morning bring me word of your unfailing love, for I have put my trust in you. Show me the way I should go, for to you I entrust my life.
>
> — Psalm 143:8 niv

This kind of relationship can only happen as we live in complete trust in who He is, what He has done, and what His priorities are in this world. If we can learn to trust His work on the cross, the fear within us that causes unbelief will dissipate. The more we can apprehend the work of His cross within our souls, the more opportunity God has to accomplish His work in and through us. We must trust what He has done and what He desires to do.

1. Read Psalm 143 and answer the following questions.

    a. What is God like?

    _____

    _____

    _____

    b. What has He done?

    _____

    _____

    _____

    c. Why can you trust Him?

    _____

    _____

    _____

_____

_____

_____

_____

Over these past weeks, many of you have seen things in your souls that have horrified and devastated you. You may have thought there was no good thing in you. It is vitally important that you move forward to embrace the love God desires to pour into your soul.

We need to understand God has marked us with a seal, the precious gift of His Spirit (Ephesians 1:13-14). Think for a moment what a seal was in the New Testament culture. When an official document was written and delivered it would be sealed with a stamp identifying its source and authority. The seal was applied or imprinted by taking a piece of wax and heating it up to soften it. The seal would then be pressed into the wax leaving a mirror image of the seal behind. This would guarantee its identity and authenticity.

Viewing your soul as the wax and God's Spirit as the seal, God has put some fire to your soul in order to soften it. His Spirit desires to press into your soul in very real ways allowing His presence to leave an imprint of the image of the Son. As His image becomes more and more deeply imprinted onto your soul, the image of the broken and wounded old self (sinful nature) melts down and His image is impressed in its place. In order for this to happen, you must allow your soul to be responsive to your God.

The Condition of Man

Many hear that Jesus died for their sins and accept the forgiveness of sin by faith, asking Him to "forgive all of their sin and come into the center of their lives." We experience salvation when we ask for forgiveness and our sincerity of heart is seen and accepted by God. However sometimes the realization of the cleansing of our sin doesn't reach to the depths of our souls. Even though we have been granted forgiveness of sin and have been made right in our standing before God, sometimes we do not experience freedom from the guilt and shame that causes us to live by the flesh. This, of course, is not because of some inadequacy in the work of Christ, but is because we do not understand the amazing work God has done for us and in us.

Often, we simply cling to the truth that God is love and wants to be our friend. Or we see Him as having removed our sin from His ledger, thus forgiving our debt and its penalty, yet we struggle to believe He has completely cleansed the sin from our soul. Sometimes our salvation seems to have been a mental theological exercise giving us our place in heaven, instead of a deep and complete cleansing of the soul. And again at times when we come to faith in Christ and ask Him to forgive us — He does, but often we fail to realize through experience what that forgiveness has done. The picture is significantly incomplete and the very things that could bring us soul-transformation are often never realized. We need to apply the Gospel of Christ to the inner man.

Applying the Gospel to the inner man is not about making sure we have confessed every sin we have ever done. That would bring works into our salvation. Applying the Gospel to the inner man is recognizing and believing what He has already done. It is about appropriating and experiencing the realization of the cleansing of forgiveness in the specific areas of our souls where the effects of sin and shame have imprinted themselves into our inner man.

Looking at what is inside is so very painful we can't believe He would require it. So often we believe if we understand and store the truth in our minds, somehow it will find its way down to our souls. Yet we need to know and experience what it means for God to remove our sin as far as the east is from the west with more than our mind. In order for that to happen, we need to look at our sin and surrender it to Him. Then we are to give up the "right" to return to our sin and focus our soul on Him. This is repentance.

Through our previous lessons, we have seen the places within our souls where unbelief has reigned. We have seen how our fear driven unbelief has worked together with life circumstances, relationships, and the shame of sin to cause us to develop ways of surviving life that are rooted in the flesh and anchored in our sin nature. Now, we must move towards true godly sorrow, which leads to repentance. Some of us are still living with the shame of our own past sins and need our soul to be freed from the bondage of shame. Some of us are living with the shame of what was done to us. Now, our reaction of shame has caused unbelief in our souls as we respond to life and people.

Behavior changes will not bring abundance to our lives. The things we run to or turn to, are what we have truly believed in and trusted to meet our need. We will need to do more than recognize the misplaced trust or unbelief. We will need to believe what God has done about the sinful nature and the flesh. It is imperative that we cling with all we are to what God has done to our old man, and how it affects our flesh.

From Belief to Trust

What about God have you failed to believe? You will need to replace any specific unbelief with specific true belief about God. Trust is moving toward or acting on what you believe. Trust is belief realized. Trust is a choice.

Some of you hunger for the intimacy God is calling you to, but it seems so intangible. The thought of giving up your independence, as well as the capacity to live and control your life is terrifying. You may even feel like God is asking you to jump off a cliff into a bottomless unknown. You cannot see the bottom or what is coming and the intangible nothingness keeps you clinging to the edge in fear. You know what God says is in the unknown. You know He claims He is there and if you trust Him He will show you wonders and mysteries beyond your dreams. You believe what He says is true, but letting go of what is solid and dependable in exchange for something you cannot see is just too much. He keeps calling you to join Him — to trust Him. You have claimed you believe He is there and from time to time you have begged Him to come out of the realm of the unknown and show Himself. In His love He has given you glimpses. He is now calling you to trust Him and abandon yourself to Him. You must choose to leave behind all you know and step into the unknown.

Forgiveness Received

Whether it is the sins of your past or the unbelief, lack of trust and survival mechanisms you respond with now, Jesus Christ the Son of God has died for them and has offered you forgiveness. Remember that forgiveness means to cancel a debt.

1. Read Ezekiel 36:24-28 and tell specifically what God has done for you. List this out point by point. This is a description of the new covenant of grace.

    _____

    _____

    _____

    _____

    _____

2. Read Ezekiel 36:29-31 and fill in the chart below.

What God will do	What we will do

If the process of cleansing requires that we remember our sin and loathe ourselves for our detestable acts and our perversion, why do we skim over this as if it weren't in God's Word? Can we experience true soul transformation apart from this? Praise God He does not leave us in a place of self-loathing. But how do we move beyond it? If we have truly seen the enormity of our sin of unbelief we will find ourselves overwhelmed with grief and self-loathing. Remember, this is the New Covenant of grace we are talking about, and godly sorrow and self-loathing are definitely a part of the process, but do we need to recall every single act of sin we have ever committed? The answer is no, but we are to deal with what God brings to our mind. Ask Him. He will show you the things still affecting your ability to live in freedom and love. He will show you the unbelief and lack of trust that is still lingering deep within and the subsequent expressions of the flesh (sin).

Forgiveness & Cleansing

How do we get past the self-loathing so we are able to delight in His abundance? We must see and understand what God has done to both forgive and cleanse us. Remember the Children of Israel had the Law and the sacrificial system to help them visualize and understand their sin and the cost of forgiveness. Now we have the cross of Christ. We must apply the reality of what Christ accomplished on the cross to the deep places within our soul.

3. Read Ezekiel 36:33-36. Explain what you believe the word pictures mean concerning your soul.

_____

_____

_____

_____

_____

4. Read the following passages and explain what Christ did to bring about your forgiveness.

   a. Hebrews 2:14-18

_____

_____

_____

_____

   b. II Corinthians 5:21

_____

_____

_____

The Struggle Within

One of the greatest hindrances to a transformed soul lies in our lack of trust in what God has done to accomplish the fullness of our salvation.

As we have said before, the Old Testament is filled with shadows of spiritual truths that have been realized in the person and work of Jesus Christ. One of the most powerful pictures of what Christ has done for us is seen in the sacrificial system given to the Children of Israel to deal with their sin and restore relationship with God. It demonstrated the enormity of sin and the holiness of God. As you look up the following passages remember and reflect on the fact that the innocent animal represents Jesus Christ. You will also find it helpful to read these passages in a modern translation. As you work through these passages, you can refer to the tabernacle graphic.

1. Read Leviticus 4:1-19 carefully. Note the meaning of the following:
    The tent of meeting referred to in this passage is the actual tent structure where the high priest would minister to God on behalf of the people and it contained the Holy of Holies where he would meet with God. The Tabernacle included the enclosed grounds surrounding the tent, where the brazen alter and basin were.

The sacrifice –
Jesus Christ

The High Priest –
Jesus Christ

The brazen altar –
The cross

Laying on of hands –
Identification with the sacrifice

2. List the step-by-step process that each participant went through.

The Worshipper	The Sacrifice	The High Priest

3. Read and summarize Hebrews 9:11-14

_____

_____

_____

_____

_____

_____

_____

It is important for you to understand what this means to your inner man. When you place your faith in Christ to forgive you of unbelief and the survival mechanisms called the flesh, God the Father has placed the penalty for all your sin upon His Son. If we have become united with Christ in His death, burial, and resurrection, then all of the shame sin brings upon us was also placed upon Him (Romans 6:1-11). Think this through. The shame from sin you have been carrying around within your soul all of this time was placed on Christ. The guilt from the perversion in your soul has been placed upon Him. The self-loathing you have experienced because of remembering your sin and recognizing all it has done to your life and to others has been laid on Him. He has taken your sin and shame; God has caused Him to "become sin" for us (II Corinthians 5:21). This means all of the guilt and shame that comes into our lives because of the sin we commit has been placed upon Him. Though Christ never sinned, He experienced the guilt and shame of your sin as if He had committed that act Himself and in that one sacrificial act has paid the penalty for all of the sin you have ever committed and will ever commit forever (Romans 6:10). Understanding this and appropriating His sacrifice is crucial for you to grieve over your sin and never return to the unbelief and fleshly survival mechanisms again.

As you stand before God, can you envision placing your sins and the shame they brought into your soul upon Him? Can you lay them on the spotless Lamb of God, Jesus Christ, and leave them on Him? Can you believe that He died with them, dealing with them forever? Can you believe the sin and shame died when He died? And was completely done away with when He defeated death and rose to life? Take a moment and contemplate all that God has done.

It is no wonder Jesus Christ has become the perfect, faithful High Priest who understands our weaknesses. It is no wonder He intercedes for us constantly. He knows what sin can do.

As we finish this look at what God has done to restore us back to Himself we need to understand what was actually accomplished.

A Look Inside

Remember, there are three needs within man that have been passed down to all generations because of the sin of Adam: spiritual significance, value and physical provision. If we are going to live in a relationship of complete trust with our Creator we must realize what He has done to meet those needs. Our God has done a mighty work!

OUR SPIRITUAL SIGNIFICANCE RESTORED

Position, Purpose and Meaning

When Christ paid the price for our sin on the cross our debt was cancelled. God no longer sees our sin, instead He sees the blood that was shed by His Son and proclaims our debt is forgiven. This is a legal and binding transaction the Bible calls a covenant – it is the Covenant of Grace. We are now seated in the place of honor and authority with Christ next to God. We now have our relationship restored and our **position with God** in heaven is secured for all eternity (Romans 6:10). This is justification.

In addition, God has included us in **His purposes** to redeem all of humankind to Himself (Ephesians 1:11; 2:10). We are to join Him in His purposes forsaking our own. When we live for His purposes and make them our own, our lives will have **eternal meaning** as we fulfill the very reason we were both created and saved.

1. Does this change your desire to seek power and position apart from God? How has your perspective of how God will meet your need for significance changed?

    _____

    _____

    _____

    _____

    _____

    _____

    _____

    _____

    _____

    _____

2. How will this be reflected in your life?

_____

_____

_____

_____

_____

_____

_____

OUR VALUE RESTORED

Love, Belonging and Being Enough

As we contemplate what Christ has done on the cross for us, we are faced with His overwhelming **sacrificial love**. He came, giving up all of heaven to become a bondservant, sacrificing His life for the sake of our restoration. To question His love seems impossible. Yet we do. He didn't just die for the whole world – He did it for you. You are His treasured possession. **You belong** next to Him. The fact that He chose you to pour value and love out on should be enough.

Remember, our value is not about us. It is about Him and His love for us. A small child will often get attached to a blanket. That child will cherish the blanket so much that they sleep with it and keep it near all the time. You would think that the blanket was made of gold thread based on how the child treats it. However, the blanket is just a piece of cloth that over time becomes ragged and dirty. Its value is established based on how much the child wants it and cares for it not on its intrinsic virtues.

God has chosen us, loved us and given us His name. He redeemed us because we belong to Him. Because He created us as He desired, **we are enough** to Him. He wants us just the way we are and He knows as we learn to trust His love we will be restored to the person He created us to be all along. He wants to be near us and loves to delight in us. When we give our lives to Him we become a new creation. When His Spirit comes to live inside of us, we learn to trust Him and live dependent on Him. We are able to fulfill the very reason we were created. By His Spirit He will enable us to accomplish His purposes as we are being renewed. This is sanctification.

1. How does this change your perspective of how God will meet your need?

_____

_____

_____
_____
_____
_____
_____
_____

2.   How will this be reflected in your life?

_____
_____
_____
_____
_____
_____
_____
_____
_____
_____

RESTORING TRUST THROUGH PROVISION

Physical Appetites, Shelter, and Safety

This arena is a little harder to understand. God will someday remove all of our need for physical provision when our bodies die physically and we are completely restored in Him. This is part of the hope we have in Christ. We will be with Him in His eternal kingdom and there will **no longer be any physical need**. This is glorification, the salvation of our bodies when He removes the very presence of sin and the death. In the mean time, He will give us the things we need to accomplish His purposes on this earth. Part of accomplishing His purposes is the transformation of our soul. He will use all things, including physical and emotional suffering, circumstances, and relationships to transform us into the image of His Son (Romans 8:28-31).

We have established that God's priorities are spiritual, eternal, and internal. God uses our need for provision to prove our trust in Him. God allows us to struggle, proving the work He has accomplished in us in a way that is obvious for those around us to see. For example, God will allow us to go through financial difficulties to prove to us and to others what we value. Do we value what God values and seek after His spiritual priorities rather than the physical ones our natural man desires? He proves our trust in Him over and over until we make His priorities our priorities. As He proves our trust in Him, others can see our response. It is not difficult to see when someone is at peace with their circumstances or is struggling to make something happen or manage the outcome.

1. How does this change your perspective of how God will meet your need?

    _____

    _____

    _____

    _____

    _____

    _____

    _____

    _____

    _____

    _____

    _____

2. How will this be reflected in your life?

    _____

    _____

    _____

    _____

    _____

    _____

    _____

    _____

    _____

    _____

    _____

Make a commitment to look back and reflect on what you have written in this lesson. Remembering what God has done and what He desires for you will help you join with His Spirit in you as He renews your mind.

The Renewed Mind
Choosing His Way 12

God's Intent

God desires that we have true, deep, immovable belief so that we are free to experience His love and the fullness He desires. He wants us to know the depths and richness of the love of Christ as we become very specific about what we believe. He wants us to move from the mental recognition of what we think we know about Him, to allow trust to rise up in our souls and embrace Him as we return to the relationship we were designed for. God longs for us to live with our souls wide open in complete abandon to Him as we walk through this life. He longs to restore us to the way we trusted and loved Him and He loved us in the Garden.

"And I pray that you, being rooted and established in love, [18] may have power, together with all the Lord's holy people, to grasp how wide and long and high and deep is the love of Christ, [19] and to know this love that surpasses knowledge—that you may be filled to the measure of all the fullness of God."

— EPHESIANS 3:17-19 NIV

In this life, we can experience a relationship where the fullness of His love is rooted deeply in our souls. And the experience of that love can be more than we could ever hope or imagine (Ephesians 3:14-21). The fullness of this relationship will be experienced when the flesh is gone and we enter His eternal kingdom of love and light!

1. Read the following passages and describe the life God is calling you to.

    a. Romans 2:4

    _____

    _____

    _____

    b. I John 1:5-10

    _____

    _____

    _____

    _____

    _____

The Condition of Man

If we desire the experience of being filled with the fullness of God, we must ask ourselves the hard questions about the fear we have and the things we have experienced in this life. We must allow the reality of what we know in our minds to move deeply into those places of fear. We must face each of those places within our soul head-on with an immovable trust in our God.

Once we determine to face the condition of our soul, we need to choose to recognize the enormity of what our unbelief has done to our souls and to those around us. We must look at what lack of trust means to our relationship with God. We need to see how God views our lack of trust so we will turn away from the emptiness that it brings.

Review *The Struggle Within* graphic.

The Struggle Within

You can see that fear produces unbelief in God and causes us to trust in ourselves instead. This is pride. Our pride causes us to believe that we have a right to have our needs met however we desire or think is best. This is entitlement and forms our priorities. When we feel we are entitled to have our needs met the way we desire we will then determine what to pursue. This is idolatry, which is then expressed through the actions of the flesh (survival mechanisms). Asking God to change the mechanisms or the actions of the flesh without understanding the source of the mechanism accomplishes nothing more than behavior modification. We can ask God to forgive us over and over for our fleshly responses and we can cry out in all sincerity, begging God to change us, but nothing will ever change until we deal with the fear and lack of trust that is at the heart of all our mechanisms.

Unbelief and lack of trust is not just a weakness. It is a sin, and the sin of unbelief will always result in expressions of the flesh. All survival mechanisms are therefore sin. It is one thing to read those words on paper, but are you willing to accept and admit, deep within your soul, that the expressions of your flesh are sin?

True repentance is the only way we will ever be free from the things that drive us away from intimacy with God and others. It can be very difficult to understand that the things we have turned to in order to survive our lives are actually sin, even the seemingly "good" things. Nonetheless, if an attitude, activity or action is a survival mechanism resulting from unbelief, it is sin. We need to admit the unbelief we operate from is, in fact, sin. *Finally, we need to repent of the sin of unbelief, our lack of trust and the actions they have caused.*

We often prefer to feel good temporarily rather than to be transformed internally and eternally (Jeremiah 6:13-15). Most of us are satisfied with a little worldly regret, but few are willing to face godly remorse, which leads to true repentance.

How important is repentance to your experience of God?

1. Look up the following verses and describe repentance and what it accomplishes.

   a. Luke 24:46-47

   _____

   _____

   _____

   b. Matthew 3:8

   _____

   _____

   _____

   c. II Corinthians 7:9-10

   _____

   _____

   _____

Remember we are not asking you to go back and repent of a specific act alone. If we repent of the lack of trust in our souls, we will experience the deep level forgiveness and cleansing that brings healing and transformation. However, if we only ask forgiveness for the act we committed, we fall far short of full repentance. We may or may not ever return to that specific sin but our lack of trust that stems from the fear within us will drive us to some other fleshly expression.

Let's consider how this might look in our lives from the examples below.

Maybe the expression of our unbelief or lack of trust in God's power has caused us to constantly pursue possessions and position for soul satisfaction and protection. As we have sought to be secure or satisfied our success has become a drive expressing itself as aggression and control. We may constantly seek to dominate others. Sometimes our drive to succeed in our career has caused us to place performance and the attainment of possessions above our relationships with our families, our church, and most importantly our God. When we pursue possessions and position we will often neglect God's purposes in our lives and can miss the reason we were created and saved. The casualties of our sin will be our families as they constantly feel our success and satisfaction is more important to us than they are. Their souls become wounded and damaged. We teach them that possessions and position are more important than people. We teach our families God's purposes are not important and our children will lead the same empty and purposeless lives we have. We cling tightly within our souls to the belief that if we don't take care of things no one else will. We deny God His place in our souls and rob Him of glory.

If we look deeply into our souls we will clearly see the perversion residing there. We must face the reality of what our sin has done to others. It is important we allow God to imprint a picture of the casualties of our sin upon our soul. We have worshipped our own abilities and success above God. Our abilities and success have become an idol like a golden calf and we bow to that image. Whatever we bow to controls us and governs our decisions.

What if when we were very young we experienced sexual abuse–and what if in that abuse we were doubly shamed by being told we were worthless if we didn't submit? We then learn, and later believe, that pleasing others is love and brings love. Our sense of value lies in our ability to meet another's need. Inevitably, we become bitter and angry as we constantly loose our value and dignity trying to please others. Even after we are saved we may change our arena of value seeking performance but the fear of not being loved and valued remains. We focus on pleasing people or looking beautiful so that we are valued and the love and acceptance of others becomes our place of idolatry.

God stands by allowing these places and the consequences they bring for a while, but now He is asking you to allow Him to remove the false things you have put in place of His presence in your inner life.

The Struggle Within

By now most of us have seen the unbelief and lack of trust that is behind our actions. We can recognize the pride, entitlement and idolatry driving our behavior or survival mechanisms. Most can see clearly the lack of trust in God and have even confessed this to Him. However, true and full repentance requires us to go even further.

The fullness of repentance comes from godly sorrow. In order to understand this part of the journey we need to define what "godly sorrow" really means.

1. Look up the word "sorrow" in your dictionary and write out the definition.

_____

_____

_____

_____

_____

The word sorrow in Greek means to experience deep inward grief. When you add the word "godly" it takes on a different meaning. The Greek phrase translated as godly sorrow means, "to grieve according to the will of God." Grief is an inconsolable sadness caused by a loss. So how do we experience inconsolable sadness over a loss according to the will of God? And what is the loss we are grieving?

Consider the areas of unbelief in your life. If you look at what the unbelief and lack of trust has done to your life through expressions of the flesh, you can begin to understand what has been lost. If you are to turn from the sin expressed through your flesh you must come to a place of deep inconsolable grief over what your sin has cost you, others and God.

To understand godly sorrow that leads to true repentance we need to look at one of the most complete pictures of godly sorrow in the Bible.

2. Read the entire chapter of Chronicles 21 and answer the questions below:

    a. What was David's sin? (vs. 1-5)

    _____

    _____

    b. What happened to David's relationship with God?

    _____

    _____

    _____

    c. What was David's response when he was confronted with his sin? (vs. 8)

    _____

    _____

    _____

    d. What would it take to remove the sin from David's soul? (vs. 11-12)

    _____

    _____

    _____

    e. What was David's response? (vs. 13)

    _____

    _____

    _____

f. What were the casualties of David's sin in the lives of others? (vs. 14)

_____

_____

_____

g. What was David's response when he saw what his sin cost others? (vs. 17)

_____

_____

_____

This is godly sorrow that leads to repentance. David's pride caused him to seek the glory for his kingdom that belonged to God. God removed His presence and His pleasure from David's life. When confronted with his sin David asked God to remove it. The word used for guilt in Hebrew means the perversion and its expressions. David saw the perversion of his soul and asked God to remove it. His request was not just about taking away his feelings of guilt. It was about soul change. It is imperative that we move beyond the need to relieve our feelings of shame to a desire for God to remove the perversion of our soul.

Notice that David grieved deeply over the consequences of his sin. The casualties of his sin were not just the 70,000 fighting men. It was every single family left without a father and husband. The casualties of our sin are often devastating to others, but most of us only think of the consequences to our own lives. Even if we believe our sin is private there are always casualties.

After we have come face to face with the fear and lack of trust within our souls we must ask God to show us how to experience grief according to His will (godly sorrow). We must grieve over what grieves God. We must see our sin as He sees it. In order to do this we must:

•   **See the magnitude of our sin.** What have you pursued to meet your core need that has replaced God in your life?

_____

_____

_____

•   Ask God to **remove the perversion** within you and the unbelief that it comes from at any and all cost. Identify that perversion and unbelief below.

_____

_____

_____

_____

_____

- **Submit** to His mighty hand. Let Him do His work in you.

- **Face the casualties** of your sin. What is the damage to your life and those around you and to your relationship with God?

_____

_____

_____

_____

_____

_____

_____

- **Take responsibility.** No more blaming others, circumstances or God. List below who and what you have blamed for your sin.

_____

_____

_____

_____

_____

_____

_____

- **Cast your soul** on the mercy of your loving God.

- Finally do what ever it takes to **make things right** with God and others. Ask God to help you see what you need to do and then list these things. Make a plan to set things right.

_____

_____

_____

_____

_____

_____

_____

Establishing Trust

Trust must be established for you to come freely before God. He needs to be able to trust you with His glory and you need to be able to come to Him without fear of condemnation. The wrong must be dealt with so you can come to Him with confidence and experience Him fully.

In every place where sin or shame is hidden within your soul you will need to do more than just give God the act of your sin. You need to do more than try to will yourself not to return to it. Part of moving on depends on understanding what reconciliation means to you and to God.

Let's begin by looking at reconciliation in terms of our human relationships. If your spouse has betrayed you or a parent has let you down you will often struggle to find peace within your soul as you relate to that person, until you are confident they have seen the magnitude of the consequences of their actions or how deeply they have hurt you. You will be unable to trust they will not repeat their actions until they see what they have done and are truly sorry for it. A simple "forgive me" or a blanket statement like "I am sorry I hurt you" doesn't establish trust. You want them to understand why and how they hurt you to begin with so they won't do it again. This is necessary for you to trust them again.

This reconciliation process is not just for your benefit. It is also for theirs. If they have not only faced what they have done and its consequences, but have also faced why they did it, they have the capacity to change. Also the experience of deep remorse relieves the shame they may keep within themselves that caused them to be distant. At that point both parties need to lay aside the past actions and move toward restoration. Restoration cannot happen until this reconciliation process has taken place. God is not petty. He is holy. He desires that you experience deep godly sorrow for your sin so you will not return to it and continuously live in a way that hinders your relationship with Him. He longs to love you and know you. He desires that you love Him and know Him. He desires deep intimacy with you and godly sorrow is the only way.

Reconciliation Through Confession

Confession is a part of the repentance process and helps to restore your relationship with God. The repentance process, which includes confession, is the New Testament fulfillment of what was accomplished when the people confessed their sin out loud as they laid their hand on the head of the animal. Confession is necessary for you to experience cleansing of your sin and shame. The word confession means to agree in your heart with God about your sin and speak that agreement out loud (1 John 1:9).

3. Read James 5:16 and record what it says about confession.

_____

_____

Talk to a trusted person. In their presence confess your sin of unbelief, lack of trust and the actions it has caused. Admit what it has done to you and others. Ask that person to pray with you and for you. Remember to confess to them your lack of trust and core drive (pride, entitlement and idolatry), not just the act or acts it has caused. Confession exposes your shame so that it cannot have power over you anymore.

Reconciliation Through Restitution

Finally, you must make things right with God and others. If you have sinned against someone or have harbored bitterness in your soul you will need to go to him or her and ask for forgiveness. You may need to seek to restore someone's reputation you have tried to destroy or if you have lied or stolen you will need to tell others and make appropriate restitution. This step is absolutely necessary for you to experience freedom from the bondage of shame.

4. Read Luke 19:2-10 and summarize what happened.

_____

_____

_____

_____

_____

5. Read Matthew 5:22-24 and record what Jesus says about reconciliation.

_____

_____

_____

_____

_____

You will need to take responsibility for your sin. This may cost you much, but the reward to your soul is beyond measure. Take the time to pray. Ask God to show you the people you may have knowingly or unknowingly hurt with your unbelief and survival mechanisms. Write out a plan to make things right. Experiencing the complete healing found in reconciliation cannot be realized apart from confession and restitution for the hurt and damage you have caused.

From Trust to Devotion

God has called you to an intimate relationship. He desires to move freely in you and through you, pouring out His love in your soul. He desires for you to know Him deeply and for you to live with such abandon to Him that you can hear His voice whispering in your ear as you journey through this life. He desires for you to know His presence not just in theory but also in emotional, spiritual and physical reality.

As belief turns to trust and His Spirit has the freedom to move through you, it will affect your relationships with others. As you begin to find your hope for love in Him you will not hold tightly in desperation to the love of others. When you experience approval and belonging in Him your ability to love others without expectations or demands grows. As you begin to trust Him completely through the experiences of your life you will find your need to control people and your environment will lessen. You will be able to rest. You will move toward loving God with abandon and others without reservation.

A Look Inside

All that we have learned is not a one-time experience. Being renewed (transformation) is an ongoing process that will require God to do a continuous work within our soul as He brings a full revelation of our already completed salvation; to our spirit, soul and eventually our bodies. We cannot make this happen but we can understand what He desires and submit to His work within us.

1. Read the following passages and summarize what God will do for the humble and contrite heart.

    a. Psalm 51:14-17

    _____
    _____
    _____

    b. Isaiah 66:2

    _____
    _____
    _____

    c. Isaiah 57:15

    _____
    _____
    _____

2. Write a prayer that expresses what you desire to have God do within you as you commit to continue to submit to the transforming power of His Spirit.

_____

_____

_____

_____

_____

_____

_____

_____

_____

_____

_____

_____

_____

_____

At the beginning of this study we stated that we would look at the things that have kept us from loving God with abandon and loving others without reservation. We have stated that loving God and others requires that we be transformed into the image of His Son. We have looked at what it means to be restored to the relationship man had with God in the Garden of Eden where man lived in a love relationship of trust as he fulfilled what God had created him to be. Now as we finish this journey we can see that God has a way to restore us to Himself and that way is to identify the areas of unbelief and lack of trust within us and choose to trust Him. As we do so He changes our perspective, which in turn changes our minds, affections, and priorities. His priorities become ours as we "put off the old self and its practices and put on the new self, which is being renewed in the knowledge of the image of its creator" from Colossians 3:10.

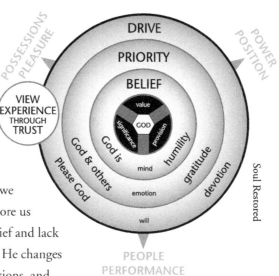

Please remember, this is a process that God will work out in us for the rest of our lives. As we learn to trust Him and are renewed to His image we will be able to reveal Him and His glory to the world. This is the very reason He both created and saved us.

Being Renewed
The Way Forward

Devotion

The very essence of devotion strives against our modern philosophies of self-empowerment and personal rights. Devotion is a word we tend to use more in reference to zealots promoting causes than of the average believer in Christ. Many people today prefer a Christianity of comfortable convenience over undying commitment.

> For as high as the heavens are above the earth, so great is his love for those who fear him; as far as the east is from the west, so far has he removed our transgressions from us.
>
> — PSALM 103:11-12 NIV

There are three basic aspects of devotion we need to cultivate within our souls so God can move freely in us and through us. They are the focus of our affections, denial of personal rights and faithfulness.

1. Our Affections

Read following the passage below with the understanding that the Greek definition of the word for "mind" actually means our heart's affection. We have replaced the word mind in this passage and inserted the phrase "heart's affection" instead.

> For those who live according to the flesh set the affections of their hearts on the things of the flesh, but those who live according to the Spirit set the affections of their hearts on the things of the Spirit.
> For to set the heart's affections on the flesh is death, but to set the heart's affection on the Spirit is life and peace. For the heart set on the flesh is hostile to God, for it does not submit to God's law; indeed, it cannot. Those who are in the flesh cannot please God.
>
> —ROMANS 8:5-8 ESV PARAPHRASE

This is not just a matter of the temporary mental focus we gain through worship music and repeating phrases or Scriptures. It is more about choosing what we delight in. What we delight in can captivate our mind and direct our drives.

How do you know the focus of your heart's affection? You can know how deeply your heart is attached to something by how much time you devote to gaining it, keeping it, and thinking about it. You will also know by how you respond at the thought of losing it or how you feel when it is threatened.

2. Loss of Personal Rights

The second part of devotion we need to understand is the loss of personal rights for the sake of another. This is probably the hardest step in all we have explored so far. Many cultures have so completely ingrained the need for personal rights in our minds that we don't even know how clouded and perverted our souls are as we cling to them. We will often surrender our individual acts of selfishness and the sin we commit to God, but to give up the "right" to run to them again is another thing entirely. We constantly beg God to take away our fleshly mechanisms but when it really comes down to it, we want to hang on to our rights to control and determine what is best for us. We will never be able to focus our affections on the Lover of our Soul until we give up our rights to hold onto what brings us pleasure or has gotten us through life's difficult times. Giving up the right to run back to our mechanisms is truly the hardest step.

Read Ruth 1:1-18 ESV

In the days when the judges ruled there was a famine in the land, and a man of Bethlehem in Judah went to sojourn in the country of Moab, he and his wife and his two sons. The name of the man was Elimelech and the name of his wife Naomi, and the names of his two sons were Mahlon and Chilion. They were Ephrathites from Bethlehem in Judah. They went into the country of Moab and remained there. But Elimelech, the husband of Naomi, died, and she was left with her two sons. These took Moabite wives; the name of the one was Orpah and the name of the other Ruth. They lived there about ten years, and both Mahlon and Chilion died, so that the woman was left without her two sons and her husband.

Then she arose with her daughters-in-law to return from the country of Moab, for she had heard in the fields of Moab that the Lord had visited His people and given them food. So she set out from the place where she was with her two daughters-in-law, and they went on the way to return to the land of Judah. But Naomi said to her two daughters-in-law, "Go, return each of you to her mother's house. May the Lord deal kindly with you, as you have dealt with the dead and with me. The Lord grant that you may find rest, each of you in the house of her husband!" Then she kissed them, and they lifted up their voices and wept. And they said to her, "No, we will return with you to your people." But Naomi said, "Turn back, my daughters; why will you go with me? Have I yet sons in my womb that they may become your husbands? Turn back, my daughters; go your way, for I am too old to have a husband. If I should say I have hope, even if I should have a husband this night and should bear sons, would you therefore wait till they were grown? Would you therefore refrain from marrying? No, my daughters, for it is exceedingly bitter to me for your sake that the hand of the Lord has gone out against me." Then they lifted up their voices and wept again. And Orpah kissed her mother-in-law, but Ruth clung to her.

And she said, "See, your sister-in-law has gone back to her people and to her gods; return after your sister-in-law." But Ruth said, "Do not urge me to leave you or to return from following you. For where you go I will go, and where you lodge I will lodge. Your people shall be my people, and your God my God. Where you die I will die, and there will I be buried. May the Lord do so to me and more also if anything but death parts me from you." And when Naomi saw that she was determined to go with her, she said no more.

Often we can consider giving up our rights for God, but when it comes to our relationship to others it is an entirely different matter. Could we give up our rights to our opinions or our desires? Can we put another person's well-being above our own regardless of their position or social status? This is truly giving up our rights.

What does it mean to put another's well-being above your own personal needs and make someone else's need a priority over your own? What does it look like in your life to set aside your right to be heard or respected? Can you give up the right to fairness and justice? What would it look like to lose your right to be loved the way you desire to be, or to lose your rights to live by your own personal strength or your right to hide your soul away when you choose? What would it be like to give up the right to choose whom and how you loved?

This concept furiously strives against many of our cultures and our own will. We must take care of ourselves because no one else will. Yet, if we are to experience the intimacy God desires for us with Him and with others, we will need to choose to give up our personal rights.

3. Faithfulness

The final part of devotion we need to understand is undying commitment or faithfulness. If we are to know God intimately and experience His presence moving through our souls we must move toward an undying commitment to Him and others. Most of you would say you have already done that. You became a Christian—isn't that commitment enough? To choose to walk forward and leave behind your rights to hold tightly to the unbelief in your soul requires a growing commitment. You must choose to surrender your soul to Living God and move forward to embrace Him with complete abandon. You must choose to love others without reservation.

Throughout this study, you have looked at the things that prevent you from experiencing the love of God deeply in your soul. You cannot give to another what you do not know yourself. Have you discovered what it is to embrace the love of God? This study and many more could never contain all that could be written on the love of God. Visualize with the eyes of your soul what it feels like to be overwhelmed by the love of God.

Allow your soul to rise up and meet the lover of your soul.

Read the prayer taken from Ephesians with the focus of your affections turned toward Him. Allow Him to pour His love into your soul.

> I pray that out of Your glorious riches You may strengthen me with power through Your Spirit in my inner being, so that Christ may dwell in my heart through faith. And I pray that You would root and establish me in Your love, so that I may have power, together with all the saints, to grasp how wide and long and high and deep is the love of Christ, and to know Your love that surpasses knowledge that I may be filled to the measure of all the fullness of God. Now to Him who is able to do immeasurably more than all I ask or imagine, according to Your power that is at work within me, to Him be glory in the church and in Christ Jesus throughout all generations, for ever and ever! Amen.
>
> — **EPHESIANS 3:16-22** PARAPHRASED

Our prayer is that you choose to abandon your soul to the Living God. To help you on your journey we would like to invite you to move forward with us. The next study in the *Finding What Matters* series examines the reference points God has given us in His Word that are designed to show us what it means to fully embrace His love. The study is called *Embracing the Love of God*. We welcome you onward.

Studies in the Finding What Matters series:

Being Renewed
Embracing the Love of God
Living with Abandon